Jekka's MEDICINAL HERBS

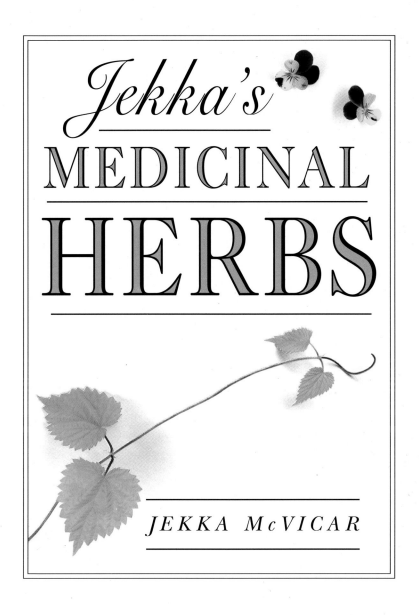

Jekka's MEDICINAL HERBS

JEKKA McVICAR

KYLE CATHIE LIMITED

To Mac

First published as *Jekka's Medicinal Herbs*
in Great Britain in 1995 by
Kyle Cathie Limited
20 Vauxhall Bridge Road, London SW1V 2SA

This edition published 1995

ISBN 1 85626 209 X

2 4 6 8 10 9 7 5 3 1

The material in this book is taken from
Jekka's Complete Herb Book

Photographs © Jessica McVicar 1994
© Michelle Garrett 1994 © Sally Maltby 1994

Artwork © Sally Maltby 1994

Book design by Geoff Hayes
Cover design by Tom Murdoch and Geoff Hayes

Printed and bound in Spain
by Graficas Reunidas, S.A., Madrid.

Jessica McVicar is hereby identified as the author of this
work in accordance with Section 77 of the Copyright,
Designs and Patents Act, 1988.

A Cataloguing in Publication record for this title is available
from the British Library.

Acknowledgements
With many thanks to Mac for all his support, Anthea for
turning up in the nick of time, Kyle for taking the gamble,
Piers for all his reading and Penny for her compliments.

Photographic acknowledgements
Plant photography by Jekka McVicar and Sally Maltby.
All other photography by Michelle Garrett.

CONTENTS

INTRODUCTION

Hippocrates said 'Let your medicine be your food, and your food your medicine.'

Herbs have been used since man has been on Earth as a food and a medicine. There are few plants capable of providing the sheer pleasure of herbs; they are the most generous of plants, aromatic and attractive, useful in both the home and the garden, health-giving and healthy.

The increasing interest in herbs is part of a movement towards a healthier lifestyle, symbolising a more natural approach. Herbs are used in cooking, in domestic products, alternative medicines and cosmetics; and they affect the quality of life in many ways.

The most extraordinary feature of herbs is their incredible versatility. You may think of a particular herb as having mainly culinary or medicinal properties and then discover it has other useful applications. Thyme for example, provides the raw material for cooking, medicines and aromatherapy.

What is a herb? It can be argued that all useful plants are herbs. The Oxford English Dictionary defines them as 'Plants of which the leaves, stem or flowers are used for food or medicine, or in some way for their scent or flavour'. To elaborate, a herb can be any plant used as an ingredient in food or drink for flavour or preservative properties, in medicine for health-giving properties, or in perfume, cosmetics or aromatherapy as a fixative, for flavour or aroma or as a cleansing agent. That herbs do you good is in no doubt, improving your health, appearance or sense of well-being.

There are records showing that herbs have been used medicinally dating back to the early Greeks. In this country in the 17th Century the Society of Apothecaries held a 'Simpleing Day' each month from April until September. The then herbal apprentices were taken out into the fields and hedgerows to learn to distinguish between the various 'simples' (herbs). Nowadays in third world countries Herbs are still the main source of medicine and in the East they are still so highly regarded that the Japanese have a new Hospital outside Tokyo which only uses Herbs and other skin practices.

Before starting a medicinal garden, or using herbs medicinally I would strongly advise you to invest in a good Herbal Medicine book which gives you medicinal recipes and instruction. When you self medicate you must respect the plant you are growing, in small doses they may be quite safe but, on the other hand, in large doses they may be harmful. So follow the recipes accurately. Always consult your doctor or a fully trained herbalist. It must be emphasised that not all illness are suitable for herbal treatment.

When planning a herb garden there are no restrictions on how it should be laid out, formally or informally, as a border, or in a pot. The only factors you must consider are: what are the soil conditions like? How sunny or shady is the area you have chosen? Would this suit the herbs you want to plant? If you find the area unsuitable for a particular herb and you have no wish to re-design your garden, plant them in containers as you will find that most herbs are accommodating plants and will grow happily in them as long as you take due consideration of their root size. This then frees you to place them in the position that most suits them and yours design, if necessary sinking the pots into the ground to disguise them. Bearing in mind that this is a medicinal herb garden you will need to plan the garden so that the plants are accessible for, depending on the medicinal preparations, you may need either the leaf, flower, stem, bark, or even the roots. So it may be necessary to leave enough room to be able to dig the plant up with out damaging its neighbour to harvest the root. I therefore suggest that one plants either in narrow beds so all the plants are accessible from the paths, or place stepping stones in the garden so that plants can be reached more easily, or, if neither of these are possible, in containers. Finally I must stress that all herbs grown for either culinary or medicinal use should, without any excuses, be grown free from the use of chemicals.

Jekka McVicar

PROPAGATION

One of the great joys of gardening is propagating your own plants. Success is dependent on adequate preparation and the care and attention you give during the critical first few weeks. The principles remain the same, but techniques are constantly changing. There is always something new to discover.

The three main methods of propagating new plants are by Seed, Cuttings and Layering.

This chapter provides general, step-by-step instructions for each of these methods. As there are always exceptions to a rule, please refer to the propagation section under each individual herb.

SEED

Sowing Outside
Most annual herbs grow happily propagated year after year from seed sown directly into the garden. There are two herbs worth mentioning where that is not the case – sweet marjoram, because the seed is so small it is better started in a pot; and basil because, in damp northern climates like that in Britain, the young seedlings will rot off.

In an average season the seed should be sown in mid- to late spring after the soil has been prepared and warmed. Use the arrival of weed seedlings in the garden as a sign that the temperature is rising. Herbs will survive in a range of different soils. Most culinary herbs originate from the Mediterranean so their preference is for a sandy free-draining soil. If your soil is sticky clay do not give up, give the seeds a better start by adding a fine layer of horticultural sand along the drill when preparing the seed bed.

Preparation of Seed Bed
Before starting, check your soil type making sure that the soil has sufficient food to maintain a seed bed. Dig the bed over, mark out a straight line with a piece of string secured tightly over each row, draw a shallow drill, 6-13mm (¼/½in) deep, using the side of a fork or hoe, and sow the seeds thinly, 2 or 3 per 25mm (1in). Do not overcrowd the bed, otherwise the seedlings will grow leggy and weak and be prone to disease.

Protected Sowing
Starting off the seeds in a greenhouse or on a windowsill gives you more control over the warmth and moisture they need, and enables you to begin propagating earlier in the season.

Nothing is more uplifting than going into the greenhouse on a cold and gloomy late-winter morning and seeing all the seedlings emerging. It makes one enthusiastic for spring.

Preparation of Seed
Most seeds need air, light, temperature and moisture to germinate. Some have a long dormancy, and some have hard outer coats and need a little help to get going. Here are two techniques.

Scarification
If left to nature, seeds that have a hard outer coat would take a long time to germinate. To speed up the process, rub the seed between 2 sheets of fine sandpaper. This weakens the coat of the seed so that moisture essential for germination can penetrate.

Stratification (vernalization)
Some seeds need a period of cold (from 1 to 6 months) to germinate. Mix the seed with damp sand and place in a plastic bag in the refrigerator or freezer. After 4 weeks sow on the surface of the compost and cover with Perlite. My family always enjoys this time of year. They go to the freezer to get the ice cream and find herb seed instead.

Preparation of Seed Container
One of the chief causes of diseased compost is a dirty propagation container. To minimize the spread of disease, remove any 'tidemarks' of compost, soil or chemicals around the insides of the pots and seed trays. Wash and scrub them thoroughly with washing up liquid, rinse with water and give a final rinse with diluted Jeyes fluid. Leave for 24 hours before re-use. Old compost also provides ideal conditions for damping off fungi and sciarid flies. To avoid cross-infection always remove spent compost from the greenhouse or potting shed.

Compost
It is always best to use a sterile seed compost. Ordinary garden soil contains many weed seeds that could easily be confused with the germinating herb seed. The compost used for most seed sowing is 50per cent propagating bark and 50per cent peat-based seed compost and unless stated otherwise within the specific herb section, this is the mix to use. However, for herbs that

Misting Unit

prefer a freer draining compost, or for those that require stratification outside, I advise using a 25 per cent peat-based seed compost: 50 per cent propagating bark and 25 per cent horticultural grit mix. And if you are sowing seeds that have a long germination period, use a soil-based seed compost.

Sowing in Seed Trays
Preparation: fill a clean seed tray with compost up to 1cm (½in) below the rim and firm down with a flat piece of wood. Do not to press too hard as this will over-compress the compost and restrict drainage, encouraging damping off disease and attack by sciarid fly.

The gap below the rim is essential, as it prevents the surface sown seeds and compost being washed over the edge when watering, and it allows room for growth when you are growing under card or glass.

Water the prepared tray using a fine rose on the watering can. Do not over-water. The compost should be damp, not soaking. After an initial watering, water as little as possible, but never let the surface dry out. Once the seed is sown lack of moisture can prevent germination and kill the seedlings, but too much water excludes oxygen and encourages damping-off fungi and root rot. Be sure to use a fine rose on the watering can so as not to disturb the seed.

Sowing Methods
There are 3 main methods, the choice dependent on the size of the seed. They are, in order of seed size, fine to large:

1 Scatter on the surface of the compost, and cover with a fine layer of Perlite.

2 Press into the surface of the compost, either with your hand or a flat piece of wood the size of the tray,

and cover with Perlite.
3 Press down to 1 seed's depth and cover with compost.

The Cardboard Trick
When seeds are too small to handle, you can control distribution by using a thin piece of card (cereal cartons are good), cut to 10cm x 5cm (4in x 2in), and folded down the middle. Place a small amount of seed into the folded card and gently tap it over the prepared seed tray. This technique is especially useful when sowing into plug trays (see below).

Sowing in Plug (Module) Trays (Multi-cell Trays)
These plug trays are a great invention. The seed can germinate in its own space, get established into a strong seedling, and make a good root ball. When potting on, the young plant remains undisturbed and will continue growing, rather than coming to a halt because it has to regenerate roots to replace those damaged in pricking out from the seed tray. This is very good for plants like coriander, which hate being transplanted and tend to bolt if you move them. Another advantage is that as you are sowing into individual cells, the problem of overcrowding is cut to a minimum, and damping-off disease and sciarid fly are easier to control. Also, because seedlings in plugs are easier to maintain, planting out or potting on is not so critical.

Plug trays come in different sizes; for example, you can get trays with very small holes of 15mm (½in) x

15mm up to trays with holes of 36.5mm (1¼in) x 36.5mm. To enable a reasonable time lapse between germination and potting on, I recommend the larger.

When preparing these trays for seed sowing, make sure you have enough space, otherwise compost seems to land up everywhere. Prepare the compost and fill the tray right to the top, scraping off surplus compost with a piece of wood level with the top of the holes. It is better not to firm the compost down. Watering in (see above) settles the compost enough to allow space for the seed and the top dressing of Perlite. For the gardener-in-a-hurry there are available in good garden centres ready-prepared propagation trays, which are plug trays already filled with compost. All you have to do is water and add the seed.

The principles of sowing in plug trays are the same as for trays. Having sown your seed, DO label the trays clearly with the name of the plant, and also the date. The date is useful as one can check their late or speedy germination. It is also good for record keeping, if you want to sow them again next year, and helps with organizing the potting on.

Seed Germination
Seeds need warmth and moisture to germinate.

The main seed sowing times are autumn and spring. This section provides general information with the table below providing a quick look guide to germination. Any detailed advice specific to a particular herb is provided in the A-Z Herb section.

Quick Germination Guide
Hot 27-32°C (80-90°F)
Rosemary

Warm 15-21°C (60-70°F)
Most plants, including those from the Mediterranean, and Chives and Parsley.

Cool 4-10°C (40-50°F)
Lavenders. (Old lavender seed will need a period of stratification).

Stratification
Arnica (old seed), Sweet Woodruff, Yellow Iris, Poppy, Soapwort, Sweet Cicely, Hops (old seed), Sweet Violet.

Scarification
All leguminous species, i.e., broom, trefoils, clovers and vetches.

Need Light (i.e., do not cover)
Chamomile, Foxglove, Thyme, Winter Savory, Poppy and Sweet Marjoram.

In a cold greenhouse, a heated propagator may be needed in early spring for herbs that germinate at warm to hot temperatures. In the house you can use a shelf near a radiator (never on the radiator), or an airing cupboard. Darkness does not hinder the germination of most herbs (see table above for exceptions), but if you put your containers in an airing cupboard YOU MUST CHECK THEM EVERY DAY. As soon as there is any sign of life, place the trays in a warm light place, but not in direct sunlight.

Hardening Off
When large enough to handle, prick out seed tray seedlings and pot up individually. Allow them to root fully.

Test plug tray seedlings by giving one or two a gentle tug. They should come away from the cells cleanly, with the root ball. If they do not, leave for another few days.

When the seedlings are ready, harden them off gradually by leaving the young plants outside during the day. Once weaned into a natural climate, either plant them directly into a prepared site in the garden, or into a larger container for the summer.

CUTTINGS

Taking cuttings is sometimes the only way to propagate (e.g. non-flowering herbs, such as **Chamomile Treneague**, and variegated forms, such as Tri-color Sage).

It is not as difficult as some people suggest, and even now I marvel at how a mere twig can produce roots and start the whole life cycle going again.

There are 4 types of cutting used in herb growing:

1 Softwood cuttings taken in spring

2 Semi-hardwood cuttings taken in summer

3 Hardwood cuttings taken in autumn

4 Root cuttings, which can be taken in spring and autumn.

For successful softwood cuttings it is worth investing in a heated propagator, which can be placed either in a greenhouse or on a shady windowsill. For success-ful semi-ripe, hardwood and root cuttings, a shaded cold frame can be used.

Softwood Cuttings
Softwood cuttings are taken from the new lush green growth of most perennial herbs between spring and mid-summer, a few examples being Balm of Gilead, Bergamot, the Chamomiles, the Mints, Prostanthera, the Rosemarys, the Scented Geraniums, the Thymes, Curly Wood Sage and Wormwood. Check under the individual herb entries in the A-Z section for more specific information.

1 The best way to get a plant to produce successful rooting material is to prune it vigorously in winter (which will encourage rapid growth when the temperature rises in the spring), and to take cuttings as soon as there is sufficient growth.

2 Fill a pot, seed tray, or plug tray with cutting compost – 50 per cent bark, 50 per cent peat. It is important to use a well-draining medium rather than standard potting mixes as, without root systems, cuttings are prone to wet rot.

Firm the compost to within 2cm (¾in) of the rim.

If space is limited or pots are unavailable, you can pack the base of several cuttings in damp sphagnum moss (rolled up firmly in a polythene strip and held in place by a rubber band or string) until the roots form.

3 Collect the cuttings in small batches in the morning. Choose sturdy shoots with plenty of leaves. Best results come from non-flowering shoots with the base leaves removed. Cut the shoot with a knife, not scissors. This is because scissors tend to pinch or seal the end of the cutting thus hindering rooting.

4 Place the cutting at once in the shade in a polythene bag or a bucket of water. Softwood cuttings are extremely susceptible to water loss; even a small loss will hinder root development. If the cuttings cannot be dealt with quickly, keep them in the cool (e.g. in a salad box from a refrigerator) to prevent excessive water loss.

5 To prepare the cutting material, cut the base of the stem 5mm (¼in) below a leaf joint, to leave a cutting of roughly 10cm (4in) long.

6 If the cutting material has to be under 10cm (4in), take the cutting with a heel. Remove the lower leaves and trim the tail which is left from the heel.

7 Trim the stem cleanly before a node, the point at which a leaf stalk joins the stem. Remove the leaves from the bottom third of the cutting, leaving at least 2 or 3 leaves on top. The reason for leaving leaves on cuttings is that the plant feeds through them as it sets root. Do not tear off the base leaves as this can cause disease; use a knife and gently cut them off.

8 Make a hole with a dibber in the compost and insert the cutting up to its leaves. Make sure that the leaves do not touch or go below the surface of the compost; they will rot away and may cause a fungus condition which can spread up the stem and to other cuttings. Do not overcrowd the container or include more than one species, because quite often they take different times to root. (For instance, keep box and thymes separate.)

Hormone rooting-powders that some gardeners use, contain synthetic plant hormones and fungicide and are not for the organic grower; following my detailed instructions you should find them unnecessary. However, they may help with difficult cuttings. The cutting should be dipped into the rooting-powder just before inserting into the compost.

9 Label and date the cuttings clearly, and only water the compost from above if necessary (the initial watering after preparing the container should be sufficient). Keep out of direct sunlight in hot weather. In fact, if it is very sunny, heavy shade is best for the first week.

Either place in a heated or unheated propagator, or cover the pot or container with a plastic bag supported on a thin wire hoop (to prevent the plastic touching the leaves), or with an upturned plastic bottle with the bottom cut off. If you are using a plastic bag, make sure you turn it inside out every few days to stop excess moisture from condensation dropping onto the cuttings.

10 Spray the cuttings every day with water for the first week. Do this in the morning, never at night. Do not test for rooting too early by tugging the cutting up, as you may disturb it at a crucial time. A better way to check for new roots is to look underneath the container. Average rooting time is 2-4 weeks.

The cutting medium is low in nutrients, so give a regular foliar feed when the cutting starts to root.

11 Harden off the cuttings gradually when they are rooted. Bring them out in stages to normal sunny, airy conditions.

12 Pot them on using a prepared potting compost once they are weaned. Label and water well after transplanting.

13 About 4-5 weeks after transplanting, when you can see that the plant is growing away, pinch out the top centre of the young cutting. This will encourage the plant to bush out, making it stronger as well as fuller.

14 Allow to grow on until a good-size root ball can be seen in the pot – check occasionally by gently removing the plant from the pot – then plant out.

Semi-hardwood Cuttings or Greenwood Cuttings
Usually taken from shrubby herbs such as Rosemary and Myrtle towards the end of the growing season (from mid-summer to mid-autumn). Use the same method (steps 2-8) as for softwood cuttings, with the following exceptions:

2 The compost should be freer-draining than for softwood cuttings, as semi-hardwood cuttings will be left for longer (see 10

below). Make the mix equal parts peat, grit and bark.

9 Follow step 9 for softwood cuttings, but place the pot, seed tray or plug tray in a cold greenhouse, cold frame, cool conservatory, or on a cold windowsill in a garage, not in a propagator, unless it has a misting unit.

10 Average rooting time for semi-hardwood cuttings is 4-6 weeks. Follow step 10 except for the watering schedule. Instead, if the autumn is exceptionally hot and the compost or cuttings seem to be drying out, spray once a week. Again, do this in the morning, and be careful not to over-water.

11 Begin the hardening off process in the spring after the frosts. Give a foliar feed as soon as there is sufficient new growth.

Hardwood Cuttings
Taken mid- to late autumn in exactly the same way as softwood cuttings steps 2-8, but with a freer draining compost of equal parts peat, grit and bark. Keep watering to the absolute minimum. Winter in a cold frame, greenhouse or conservatory. Average rooting time can take as long as 12 months.

Root Cuttings
This method of cutting is suitable for plants with creeping roots, such as Bergamot, Comfrey, Horseradish, Lemon Balm, Mint. Soapwort and Sweet Woodruff.

1 Dig up some healthy roots in spring or autumn.

2 Fill a pot, seed tray or plug tray with cutting compost – 50 per cent bark, 50 per cent peat, firmed to within 3cm (1in) of the rim. Water well and leave to stand while preparing your cutting material.

3 Cut 4-8cm (1.5-3in) lengths of root that carry a

growing bud. It is easy to see the growing buds on the roots of mint.

This method is equally applicable for all the varieties mentioned above as suitable for root propagation, with the exception of Comfrey and Horseradish, where one simply slices the root into sections, 4-8cm (1½-3in) long, using a sharp knife to give a clean cut through the root. Do not worry, each will produce a plant!
These cuttings lend themselves to being grown in plug trays.

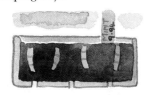

4 Make holes in the compost with a dibber. If using pots or seed trays these should be 3-6cm (1-2½in) apart. Plant the cutting vertically.

5 Cover the container with a small amount of compost, followed by a layer of Perlite level with the top of the container.

6 Label and date. This is most important because you cannot see what is in the container until the plant begins to grow and it is all too easy to forget what you have planted.

7 Average rooting time 2-3 weeks. Do not water until roots or top growth appears. Then apply liquid feed.

8 Slowly harden off the cuttings when rooted.

9 Pot on in a potting

compost once they are weaned. Label and water well after transplanting. You can miss this stage out if you have grown the root cuttings in plug trays.

10 About 2-3 weeks after transplanting, when you can see that the plant is growing away, pinch out the top centre of the young cutting. This will encourage the plant to bush out, making it stronger as well as fuller.

11 Allow to grow on until a good-size root ball can be seen in the pot. Plant out in the garden when the last frosts are over.

LAYERING

If cuttings are difficult to root you can try layering, a process that encourages sections of plant to root while still attached to the parent. Bay, Rosemary, Sage are good examples of plants that suit this method.

1 Prune some low branches off the parent plant during the winter season to induce vigorous growth and cultivate the soil around the plant during winter and early spring by adding peat and grit to it.

2 Trim the leaves and side shoots of a young vigorous stem for 10-60cm (4-24in) below its growing tip.

3 Bring the stem down to ground level and mark its position on the soil. Dig a trench at that point, making one vertical side 10-15cm (4-6in) deep, and the other sloping towards the plant.

4 Roughen the stem at the point where it will touch the ground.

5 Peg it down into the trench against the straight side, then bend the stem at right angles behind the growing tip, so that it protrudes vertically. Then

return the soil to the trench to bury the stem. Firm in well.

6 Water well using a watering can and keep the soil moist, especially in dry periods.

7 Sever the layering stem from its parent plant in autumn if well rooted, and 3-4 weeks later nip out the growing tip from the rooted layer to make plant bush out.

8 Check carefully that the roots have become well established before lifting the layered stem. If necessary, leave for a further year.

9 Replant either in the open ground or in a pot using the bark, grit, peat mix of compost. Label and leave to establish.

Mound Layering
A method similar to layering that not only creates new growth but also improves the appearance of old plants. This is particularly suitable for sages and thymes, which can woody in the centre.

1 In the spring, pile soil mixed with peat and sand over the bare woody centre until only young shoots show.

2 By late summer, roots will have formed on many of these shoots. They can be taken and planted in new locations as cuttings or by root division.

3 The old plant can then be dug up and disposed of.

PESTS AND DISEASES

Herbs suffer from few pests and diseases, and in fact many of them can be used in the vegetable garden to protect other crops. Even so, always be on the lookout, as, in early stages of attack, they can often be dealt with by methods other than the dreaded spray gun.

GENERAL METHODS OF CONTROL

Biological Control
Many biological control methods are now available commercially. When you plant in the open, harmful pests are mostly kept under control by predators. However, in the enclosed environment of the greenhouse, the natural balance can break down. All biological control methods are relatively expensive when compared with the chemical alternatives, and nearly all are dependent on warm temperatures to work efficiently.

Organic sprays
If all else fails, there are now organic sprays for pests such as green- and whitefly, which can be purchased at any good garden centre or hardware shop. Make sure that it is an organic spray with the recognized organic symbol. We use a liquid soap called Savona, which is mixed with rainwater and sprayed on infestations of white- or greenfly. It is harmless to ladybirds, bees and other insects.

There are no organic fungicides on the market, but elder leaf is an old remedy worth trying against mildew. Spray it onto the leaves.Also, chamomile makes a good spray against the damping-off diseases in young plants.

Companion Planting
I believe that certain plants can assist other plants to thrive when planted together.

Fragrant herbs such as hyssop, thyme, marjoram, chives and parsley are beneficial in maintaining the health of a vegetable garden. There are no scientific records to back this up, but a number of gardeners have reported improvements in the general health of their vegetables when inter-planted with these herbs.

Many herbs act as an insect repellent when grown near other plants, a reason being the scent they give off. The most effective ones are *tansy, pennyroyal, nasturtiums, stinging nettle, garlic, chives, hyssop, wormwood* and *southernwood.*

Using herbs as an insecticide must be effective, because if you read this book carefully you will see that many can kill if used incorrectly. *Pyrethrum* is already used in insecticides and there are a number of others identified in the A-Z of Herbs, which can also be used in various ways. I am sure that there must be others waiting to be discovered.

Chemicals for Control of Pests and Diseases
I realize that some people need to use chemicals. However, most herbs can be grown very successfully without, and if the herbs are being used as a food crop, it is worth taking that little bit of extra care.

When choosing chemicals, choose the one appropriate to the problem. Follow the manufacturer's instructions carefully. Store the bottle after use in a secure cupboard, away from animals and children.

PESTS

There are many, many pests and I have only mentioned the few that are known to affect herbs in general.

Aphids. Greenfly, Blackfly, Black Bean Aphid
From early spring in the greenhouse, and later outside, keep a watch for greenfly. If you see a few, kill them! If there are a lot, spray them with a horticultural soap, following the manufacturer's instructions.

With blackfly, do exactly the same. Do not use a high pressure hose as you will damage the plant. If it is a pot plant, such as nasturtiums, wash them off gently under the tap; otherwise spray with a horticultural soap, as above.

Borage and runner beans thrive side by side as companion plants

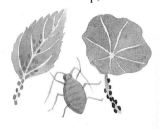

Carrot Fly

The grub of this fly tunnels into the roots of plants during early summer, so herbs such as those from the Umbelliferous family, which have a long tap root, are at risk. The first sign of attack will be the yellowing or whitling of the leaves and any stunted growth. Parsley may be particularly vulnerable, and in this case the plant should be pulled up and destroyed to get rid of the pests. However, large herbs should overcome attacks, so just pick off dead leaves and boost the plant by feeding with liquid seaweed. A preventative method is to put a 75cm (30in) polythene barrier around the crop during mid-spring, or cover with agricultural fleece while the plants are young. Sowings after mid-summer should miss the first flies.

Caterpillars Cabbage White

These are attracted to herbs with large leaves, such as horse-radish, in late spring through to early autumn. Check weekly, and simply pick them off by hand and destroy. Early in the season, when the plants are small, agricultural fleece is a good barrier.

Leaf Miners

These grubs are sometimes a problem on lovage, wild celery, certain sorrels and various mints. They eat through the leaf, creating winding tunnels in the leaves like little silver tracks, which are clearly visible. Watch for the first tunnels, pick off the affected leaves and destroy them. If left, the tunnels will extend into broad dry patches, and complete leaves will wither away.

Red Spider Mite

The spider mites like hot dry conditions and can become prolific in a glasshouse. Look out for early signs of the pests such as speckling on the upper surfaces of the leaves. Look under the leaf with a magnifying glass and you will see these minute red spiders. Another tell-tale sign is the cobwebs. At first sight, either use horticultural soap in the form of a spray, or the natural predator *Phytoseiulus persimilis*, following the instructions that will come with them. Do not use both.

Scale Insects

These are often notice-able as im-mobile, waxy, brown/yellow, flat, oval lumps gathered on the backs of leaves or on the stems of bay trees. These leaves also become covered with sticky black sooty mould. Rub off the scales gently before the infestation builds up. Alternatively, use a horticultural liquid soap, following the manufacturer's instructions.

Slugs

These can only be got rid of by hand or by setting out beer traps, even better a size 10 welly boot. There is a microscopic worm that can be used as a form of biological control and infects the slugs with a bacterium that stops them feeding within a week, it actually kills them in two. This is an expensive way of getting rid of them, but worth it to protect your specimen plants.

Vine Weevil

These can be a major pest. Look out for them in the spring and early autumn. In the ground or in pots you may see horrid white grubs with orange heads. The parent is a small nocturnal beetle with a weevil's nose. The grubs eat the roots of plants, the beetles eat leaves, especially those of vines. I have tried various organic methods of irradication, from re-potting 10,000 plants to check and get rid of the grubs, to watering with a *nematodes* (eelworms) in the autumn. This is a form of biological control the worms destroy the vine weevil grub. The temperature must be warm for them to work. The best is still a size 10 welly.

White Fly

Under protection in the glasshouse this can be a problem, less so outside. It is essential to act immed-ately, either by introducing the natural predator *Encarsia formosa*, a minute parasitic wasp that lays its eggs in the whitefly larvae, which is usually found attached to the underside of the leaves. Unfortunately, these parasites need warm temperatures to multiply so they cannot be successfully used in early spring or autumn. Alternatively, spray with a horticultural soap and repeat 7 days later.

DISEASE

Mint Rust (& other similar diseases)

Plants affected by rust should be dug up and thrown away. Alternatively, you can, in the autumn, put straw around the affected plants and set it alight. This will actually sterilize the soil and the plant. Comfrey suffers from a similar rust disease. Here the best answer is to keep the plant clipped. Cut off leaves every 4 weeks and keep well fed with manure and compost.

Powdery Mildew

This common fungal disease can occur when the conditions are hot and dry, and the plants are overcrowded. Prevent it by watering well during dry spells, following the recommended planting distances, and clearing away any fallen leaves in the autumn. Adding a mulch in the autumn or early spring also helps. If your plant does suffer, destroy all the affected leaves before spraying with elder.

Harvesting

The more you pick the healthier the plant. People are told that if their chives start to flower they will have no more fresh leaves until the following year. Rubbish! Pick some of the flowers to use in salads and, if the plant is then cut back to within 4cm (1½in) of the ground and given a good feed of liquid fertilizer, it will produce another crop of succulent leaves within a month. Keep two chive plants: one for flowering and one for harvesting.

Herbs can be harvested from very early on in their growing season. This encourages the plant to produce vigorous new growth. It allows the plant to be controlled both in shape and size. Most herbs reach their peak of flavour just before they flower. Snip off suitable stems early in the day before the sun is fully up, or even better on a cloudy day (provided it is not too humid). Cut whole stems rather than single leaves or flowers. Always use a sharp knife, sharp scissors or secateurs, and cut lengths of 5–8cm (2–3in) from the tip of the branch, this being the new soft growth. Do not cut into any of the older, woody growth. Cut from all over the plant, leaving it looking shapely. Pick herbs which are clean and free from pests and disease; they should not be discoloured or damaged in any way. If herbs are covered in garden soil, sponge them quickly and lightly with cold water, not hot as this will draw out the oils prematurely. Pat dry as quickly as possible. Keep each species separately so that they do not contaminate each other. Do not be greedy!

HARVESTING

Annual herbs

Most can be harvested at least twice during a growing season. Cut them to within 10–15cm (4–6in) of the ground, and feed with liquid fertilizer after each cutting. Do not cut the plants too low in the first harvesting as they will not be able to recover in time to give a further cutting later on. Give annuals their final cut of the season before the first frosts; they will have stopped growing some weeks before.

Perennial herbs

In the first year of planting, perennials will give one good crop; thereafter it will be possible to harvest two or three times during the growing season. Do not cut into the woody growth unless deliberately trying to prevent growth; again, cut well before frosts as cutting late in the season may weaken plants and inhibit them from surviving the winter. There are of course exceptions; sage is still very good after frosts, and both thyme and golden marjoram (with some protection) can be picked gently even in mid-winter.

Flowers and seeds

Pick flowers for drying when they are barely opened. Seed should be collected as soon as you notice a change in colour of the seed pod; if when you tap the pod a few scatter on the ground, it is the time to gather them. Seeds ripen very fast, so watch them carefully.

Roots

These are at their peak of flavour when they have completed a growing season. Dig them through autumn as growth ceases. Lift whole roots with a garden fork, taking care not to puncture or bruise the outer skin. Wash them free of soil. Cut away any remains of top growth and any fibrous off-shoots. For drying cut large, thick roots in half length-ways and then into smaller pieces for ease.

Individual herbs laid out for drying

DRYING

The object of drying herbs is to eliminate the water content of the plant quickly and, at the same time, to retain the essential oils. It looks pretty to have bunches of herbs hanging up in a kitchen but most of the flavour will be lost quickly. Herbs need to be dried in a warm, dark, dry and well-ventilated place. The faster they dry, the better retained are the aromatic oils. Darkness helps to prevent loss of colour and unique flavours. The area must be dry, with a good air flow, to hasten the drying process and to discourage mould.

Suitable places for drying herbs include:
* an airing cupboard

* attic space immediately under the roof (provided it does not get too hot)
* in the oven at low temperature and with the door ajar (place the herbs on a brown piece of paper with holes punched in it and check regularly that the herbs are not over-heating
* a plate-warming compartment
* a spare room with curtains shut and door open.

The temperature should be maintained at slightly below body temperature, between 21–33°C/70–90°F.

Herbs should always be dried separately from each other, especially the stronger scented ones like lovage. Spread them in a single layer on trays or slatted wooden racks covered with muslin or netting. The trays or frames should be placed in the drying areas so that they have good air circulation. Herbs need to be turned over by hand several times during the first two days.

Roots require a higher temperature – from 50–60°C/120–140°F. They are quicker and easier to dry in an oven and require regular turning until they are fragile and break easily. Specific requirements are given for each herb in the A–Z section.

Seed should be dried without any artificial heat and in an airy place. Almost-ripe seed heads can be hung in paper bags (plastic causes them to sweat) so the majority of seeds will fall into the bag as they mature. They need to be dried thoroughly before storing and the process can take up to two weeks.

TIP: An alternative method for flowers, roots or seed heads is to tie them in small bundles of 8 to 10 stems. Do not pack the stems too tightly together, as air needs to circulate through and around the bunches. Then hang them on coat-hangers in an airy, dark room until they are dry.

The length of drying time varies from herb to herb, and week to week. The determining factor is the state of the plant material. If herbs are stored before drying is complete, moisture will be reabsorbed from the atmosphere and the herb will soon deteriorate. Leaves should be both brittle and crisp. They should break easily into small pieces but should not reduce to a powder when touched. The roots should be brittle and dry right through. Any softness or sponginess means they are not sufficiently dry and, if stored that way, will rot.

A QUICK METHOD OF HERB DRYING

Microwave manufacturers have said it takes 3 to 4 minutes to dry thoroughly 10 sprigs of any herb! I have tried. It is easy to over-dry and cook the leaves to the point of complete disintegration. I have found that small-leafed herbs such as rosemary and thyme take about 1 minute, whilst the larger, moist leaves of mint dry in about 3 minutes. Add an eggcupful of water to the microwave during the process. **And be warned! Sage can ignite . . .**

STORING

Herbs lose their flavour and colour if not stored properly. Pack the leaves or roots, not too tightly, into a dark glass jar with an air-tight screw top. Label with name and date. Keep in a dark cupboard; nothing destroys the quality of the herb quicker at this stage than exposure to light.
After the initial storing, keep a check on the jars for several days. If moisture

Parsley stored in a bag for freezing, together with ice cubes for convenience

starts to form on the inside of the container, the herbs have not been dried correctly. Return them to the drying area and allow further drying time.

Most domestic herb requirements are comparatively small so there is little point in storing large amounts for a long time. The shelf life of dried herbs is only about 1 year so it is sufficient to keep enough just for the winter.

Dried herbs are usually 3 to 4 times more powerful than fresh. When a recipe calls for a tablespoon of a fresh herb and you only have dried use a teaspoonful.

TIP: If you have large dark jars, thyme and rosemary can be left on the stalk. This makes it easier to use them in casseroles and stews and to remove before serving.

FREEZING HERBS

Freezing is great for culinary herbs as colour, flavour and the nutritional value of the fresh young leaves are retained. It is becoming an increasingly popular way to preserve and store culinary herbs, being quick and easy. I believe it is far better to freeze herbs such as fennel, dill,, parsley, tarragon and chives than to dry them.

Pick the herbs and, if necessary, rinse with cold water, and shake dry before freezing, being careful not to bruise the leaves. Put small amounts of herbs into labelled, plastic bags, either singly, or as a mixture for bouquet garnis. Either have a set place in the freezer for them or put the bags into a container, so that they do not get damaged with the day-to-day use of the freezer.

There is no need to thaw herbs before use; simply add them to the cooking as required. For chopped parsley, freeze the bunches whole in bags and, when you remove them from the freezer, crush the parsley in its bag with your hand. Do not be distracted in this task or you will have a herb that has thawed and is a limp piece of greenery. This technique is good for all fine-leaved herbs.

Another way to freeze herbs conveniently is to put finely-chopped leaves into an ice-cube tray and top them up with water. The average cube holds 1 tablespoon chopped herbs and 1 teaspoon water.

TIP: The flowers of borage and the leaves of the variegated mints look very attractive when frozen individually in ice-cubes for drinks or fruit salads.

HERB DYE CHART

Herbs have been used to dye cloth since earliest records. In fact, until the 19th century and the birth of the chemical industry, all dyes were 'natural'. Then the chemical process, offering a larger range of colours and a more guaranteed result, took over. Now, once again, there is a real demand for more natural products and colours, which has resulted in a revival of interest in plants as a dye source.

The most common dyeing herbs are listed in the dye chart. You will notice that yellows, browns and greys are predominant. Plenty of plant material will be required so be careful not to over-pick in your own garden (and **please** do not pick other people's plants without permission! I plead from personal experience). To begin with, keep it simple. Pick the flowers just as they are coming out, the leaves when they are young and fresh and a good green; dig up roots in the autumn and cut them up well before use.

DYE CHART

Common Name	Botanical Name	Part Used	Mordant	Colour
Comfrey	Symphytum officinale	Leaves and stalks	Alum	Yellows
Chamomile, Dyer's	Anthemis tinctoria	Flowers	Alum	Yellows
Chamomile, Dyer's	Anthemis tinctoria	Flowers	Copper	Olives
Elder	Sambucus nigra	Leaves	Alum	Greens
Elder	Sambucus nigra	Berries	Alum	Violets/Purple
Golden Rod	Solidago canadensis	Whole plant	Chrome	Golden Yellows
Horsetail	Equisetum arvense	Stems and leaves	Alum	Yellows
Juniper	Juniperus communis	Crushed berries	Alum	Yellows
Marigold	Calendula officinalis	Petals	Alum	Pale Yellow
Meadowsweet	Filipendula ulmaria	Roots	Alum	Black
Nettle	Utrica dioica	Whole plant	Copper	Greyish green
St John's Wort	Hypericum perforatum	Flowers	Alum	Beiges
Sorrel	Rummex acetosa	Whole plant	Alum	Dirty yellow
Sorrel	Rummex acetosa	Roots	Alum	Beige/pink
Tansy	Tanacetum vulgare	Flowers	Alum	Yellows
Woad	Isatus tinctoria	Leaves	Sodium dithionite, ammonia	Blues

FABRIC

Any natural material can be dyed; some are more tricky than others. It just takes time and practice. In the following sections I will explain the techniques connected with dying wool, the most reliable and easiest of natural materials. Silk, linen and cotton can also be dyed, but are more difficult.

PREPARATION

First time, this is a messy and fairly lengthy process, so use a utility room, or clear the decks in the kitchen and protect all areas. Best of all keep it away from the home altogether. Some of the mordants used for fixing dye are poisonous, so keep them well away from children, pets and food.

The actual dyeing process is not difficult, but you will need a few special pieces of equipment, and space.

1 large stainless steel vessel, such as a preserving can (to be used as the dye-bath)
1 stainless steel or enamel bucket and bowl
1 pair of tongs (wooden or stainless steel; to be used for lifting)

PREPARATION OF DYE

No two batches of herbal dye will be the same. There are so many variable factors – plant variety, water, mordant, immersion time.

The amount of plant material required for dyeing is very variable. A good starting ratio is 500g (1lb) of mordanted wool in skeins to 500g (1lb) plant material.

* Chop or crush the plant material.
* Place loosely in a muslin or nylon bag and tie securely .
* Leave to soak in 20 litres (4 gallons) of soft tepid water overnight.
* Slowly bring the water and herb material to the boil.
* Reduce heat and simmer at 82-94°C (180-200°F) for as long as it takes to get the water to the desired colour. This can take from 1 to 3 hours.
* Remove the pan from the heat, remove the herb material, and allow the liquid to cool to hand temperature.

DYEING PROCESS

* Gently add the wool.
* Bring the water slowly to the boil, stirring occasionally with the wooden tongs.
* Allow to simmer for a further hour.
* Remove pan from the heat and leave the wool in the dye-bath until cold, or until the colour is right.
* Remove the wool with the tongs and rinse in tepid water until no colour runs out.
* Give a final rinse in cold water.
* Dry the skeins of wool over a rod or cord, away from direct heat. Tie a light weight to the bottom to stop the wool kinking during the drying process.

---

1 measuring jug
1 pair rubber gloves essential for all but Jumblies – 'Their heads are green and their hands are blue, And they went to sea in a sieve.'
Pestle and mortar
Thermometer
Water; this must be soft, either rainwater or filtered
Scales

Dyeing comprises four separate tasks –
* Preparation of material (known as scouring)
* Preparation of Mordant
* Preparation of Dye
* Dyeing Process

PREPARATION OF THE MATERIAL (SCOURING)

Prepare the wool by washing it in a hot solution of soap flakes or a proprietary scouring agent in order to remove any grease. Always handle the wool gently. Rinse it several times, squeezing (gently) between each rinse. On the final rinse add 50ml (2fl oz) of vinegar.

PREPARATION OF THE MORDANT

Mordants help 'fix' the dye to the fabric. They are available from chemists or dye suppliers. The list below includes some of the more common. Some natural dyers say that one should not use mordants, but without them the dye will run very easily.

Alum: Use 25g (1oz) to 500g (1lb) dry wool
This is the most useful of mordants, its full title being Potassium aluminium sulphate. Sometimes potassium hydrogen tartrate, cream of tartar, is added (beware! this is not the baking substance) in order to facilitate the process and brighten the colour.

Iron: Use 5g (⅛oz) to 500g (1lb) dry wool
This is ferrous sulphate. It dulls and deepens the colours. It is added in the final process after first using the mordant Alum. Remove the wool before adding the iron, then replace the wool and simmer until you get the depth of colour required.

Copper: Use 15g (½oz) to 500g (1lb) dry wool
This is copper sulphate. If you mix with 300ml (½ pint) of vinegar when preparing the mordant it will give a blue/green tint to colours. WARNING: Wear gloves; copper is poisonous.

Chrome: Use 15g (½oz) to 500g (1lb) dry wool
This is bichromate of potash and light-sensitive, so keep it in the dark. It gives the colour depth, makes the colours fast, and gives the wool a soft, silky feel. WARNING: Wear gloves; chrome is poisonous.

* Dissolve the mordant in a little hot water.
* Stir into 20 litres (4 gallons) of hot water 50°C (122°F).
* When thoroughly dissolved immerse the wet, washed wool in the mixture. Make sure it is wholly immersed.
* Slowly bring to the boil and simmer at 82-94°C (180-200°F) for an hour.
* Remove from the heat. Take the wool out of the water and rinse.

NATURAL DYE GARDEN

There has been a marked increase of interest in plants as a dye source, which is not surprising since they offer a subtle range of rich colours.

This garden includes a representative selection of those dyes that can be easily grown. It is designed with separate beds because you will need a fairly large quantity of each herb to produce the dye, and the beds make it easy to harvest the leaves, flowers and roots. You should allow sufficient space between the beds for access and maintenance.

The eight herbs I have selected give a broad range of colours. As the marigolds and the parsley are shortlived you may like to replace them with woad or even nettles. For more choice of plants, see the section on Natural Dye.

When choosing which plant goes where, the only important consideration is that the elder will grow into a fairly large tree, so plant it where it will not get in the way of the other plants or spoil the sightlines of your garden. In the present design, you will note that all with the exception of the elder die back into the ground in winter. Autumn is therefore an ideal time to give all the herbs, including the elder, a good mulch of well-rotted manure.

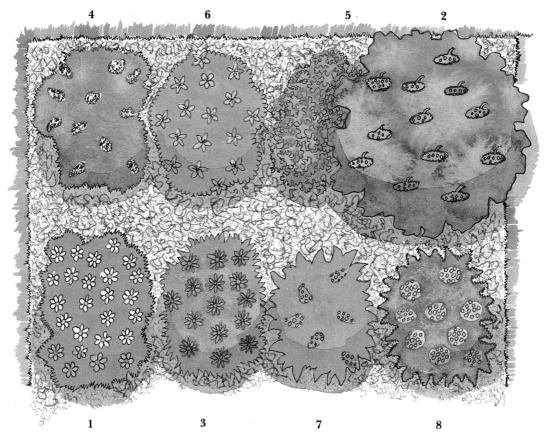

Herb	Part	Mordant	Colour
1 Chamomile, dyers *Anthemis tinctoria*	Flowers	Alum	Bright yellow
	Flowers	Copper	Olive
2 Elder *Sambucus nigra*	Leaves	Alum	Green
	Berries	Alum	Violet/purple
3 Marigold *Calendula officinalis*	Petals	Alum	Pale yellow
4 Meadowsweet *Filipendula ulmaria*	Roots	Alum	Black
5 Parsley *Petroselinum crispum*	Fresh leaves	Alum	Cream
6 St John's Wort *Hypericum perforatum*	Flowers	Alum	Beige
7 Sorrel *Rumex acetosa*	Whole plant	Alum	Pale dirty yellow
8 Tansy *Tanacetum vulgare*	Flowers	Alum	Yellows

MEDICINAL HERB GARDEN

I would like this garden, not just for its medicinal use, but for the tranquillity it would bring. The choice of herbs is not only for internal use but for the whole being. I can imagine sitting on the seat watching the dragonflies playing over the pond.

Some of the herbs included are certainly not for self-administration, for instance blue flag iris, but this is a beautiful plant and would look most attractive with the meadowsweet and the valerian. Chamomile, peppermint, dill and lemon balm are easy to self-administer with care as they all make beneficial teas. One should not take large doses just because they are natural, as some are very powerful. I strongly advise anyone interested in planting this garden to get a good herbal medicine book, see a fully trained herbalist, and always consult your doctor about a particular remedy.

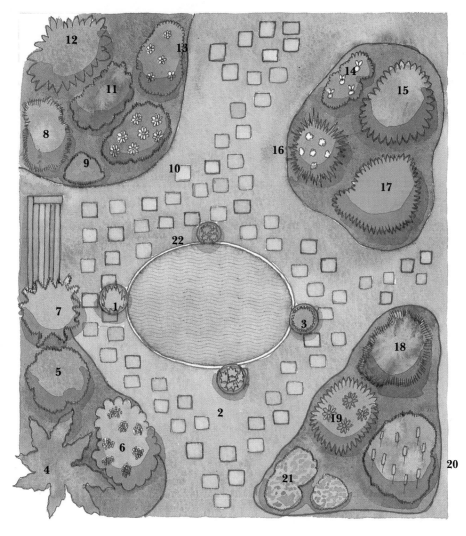

1	**Blue Flag Iris** *Iris versicolor*	12	**Feverfew** *Tanacetum parthenium*
2	**Meadowsweet** *Filipendula ulmaria*	13	**Heartsease** *Viola tricolor*
3	**Valerian** *Valeriana officinalis*	14	**Lemon Balm** *Melissa officinalis*
4	**Horseradish** *Armoracia rusticana*	15	**Garlic** *Allium sativum*
5	**Sage** *Salvia officinalis*	16	**Peppermint** *Mentha x piperita*
6	**Lady's Mantle** *Alchemilla mollis*	17	**Fennel** *Foeniculum vulgare*
7	**Rosemary** *Rosmarinus officinalis*	18	**Pot Marigold** *Calendula officinalis*
8	**Dill** *Anethum graveolens*	19	**Lavender Seal** *Lavandula x intermedia* 'Seal'
9	**Chamomile** *Chamaemelum nobile*	20	**Thyme Garden** *Thymus vulgaris*
10	**Horehound** *Marrubium vulgare*	21	**Houseleek** *Sempervivum tectorum*
11	**Comfrey** *Symphytum officinale*		

Achillea millefolium

YARROW

Also known as Nosebleed, Millefoil, Thousand Leaf, Woundwort, Carpenter's Weed, Devil's Nettle, Mille Foil, Soldier's Woundwort and Noble Yarrow. From the family Compositae.

Yarrow is found all over the world in waste places, fields, pastures and meadows. It is common throughout Europe, Asia and North America.

This is another very ancient herb. It was used by the Greeks to control haemorrhages, for which it is still prescribed in homeopathy and herbal medicine today. The legend of Achilles refers to this property – it was said that during the battle of Troy, Achilles healed many of his warriors with yarrow leaves. Hence the name, 'Achillea'.

It has long been considered a sacred herb. Yarrow stems were used by the Druids to divine seasonal weather.The ancient Chinese text of prophecy, *I Ching*, The Book of Changes, states that 52 straight stalks of dried yarrow, of even length, were spilled instead of the modern way of using 3 coins.

It was also associated with magic. In Anglo-Saxon times it was said to have a potency against evil, and in France and in Ireland it is one of the Herbs of St John. On St John's Eve, the Irish hang it up in their houses to avert illness.

There is an old superstition, which apparently still lingers in remote parts of Britain and the United States, that if a young girl tickles her nostrils with sprays of yarrow and her nose starts to bleed, it proves her lover's fidelity:

'Yarrow away, Yarrow away, bear a white blow?
If my lover loves me, my nose will bleed now.'

Yarrow *Achillea millefolium*

SPECIES

Achillea millefolium
Yarrow
Hardy perennial. Ht 30-90cm (1-3ft), spread 60cm (2ft) and more. Small white flowers with a hint of pink appear in flat clusters from summer to autumn. Its specific name, **millefolium**, means 'a thousand leaf', which is a good way to describe these darkish green, aromatic, feathery leaves.

Achillea millefolium 'Fire King'
Hardy perennial. Ht and spread 60cm (24in). Flat heads of rich, red, small flowers in flat clusters all summer. Masses of feathery dark green leaves. This has an upright habit and is a vigorous grower.

Achillea 'Coronation Gold'
Hardy perennial. Ht 1m (3ft), spread 60cm (2ft). Large flat heads of small golden flowerheads in summer that dry well for winter decoration. Masses of feathery silver leaves.

Achillea Moonshine
Hardy perennial. Ht 60cm (24in), spread 50cm (20in). Flat heads of bright yellow flowers throughout summer. Masses of small feathery grey/green leaves.

CULTIVATION

Propagation
Seed

For reliable results sow the very small seed under cool protection in autumn. Use either a proprietary seeder or the cardboard trick and sow into prepared seed or plug trays. Leave the trays in a cool greenhouse for the winter. Germination is erratic. Harden off and plant out in the garden in spring. Plant 20-30cm (8-12in) apart, remembering that it will spread. As this is an invasive plant, I do not advise sowing direct into the garden.

Division

Yarrow is a prolific grower, producing loads of creeping rootstock in a growing season. To stop the invasion, divide by digging up a clump and replanting where required. In the spring or early autumn.

Pests and Diseases

Yarrow is free from both.

Maintenance

Spring: Divide established clumps.
Summer: Dead-head flowers, and cut back after flowering to prevent self-seeding.
Autumn: Sow seeds. Divide established plants.
Winter: No need for protection, very hardy plant.

Garden Cultivation

Yarrow is one of nature's survivors. Its creeping rootstock and ability to self-seed ensure its survival in most soils.

It does well in seaside gardens, as it is drought-tolerant. Still, owners of manicured lawns will know it as a nightmare weed that resists all attempts to

Salad made with 3 Wild herbs

irradicate it.

Yarrow is the plant doctor of the garden, its roots secretions activating the disease resistance of nearby plants. It also intensifies the medicinal actions of other herbs and deepens their fragrance and flavour.

Harvest

Cut the leaves and flowers for drying as the plant comes into flower.

CONTAINER GROWING

Yarrow itself does not grow well in containers. However, the hybrids, and certainly the shorter varieties, can look stunning. Use the bark, grit, peat mix of compost and feed plants with liquid fertilizer during the flowering season, following the manufacturer's instructions. Cut back after flowering and keep watering to a minimum in winter. No varietiy is suitable for growing indoors.

CULINARY

The young leaves can be used in salads. Here is an interesting salad recipe:

Salad made with 3 Wild Herbs

Equal parts of yarrow, plantain and water cress
A little garlic
½ cucumber
Freshly chopped or dried chives and parsley
1 medium, boiled cold potato
Salad dressing consisting of lemon and cream, or lemon and oil, or lemon and cream and a little apple juice.

Select and clean herbs. Wash carefully and allow to drain. Cut the yarrow and plantain into fine strips. Cube cucumber and potato into small pieces. Leave watercress whole and arrange in bowl. Add herbs and other vegetables and salad dressing and mix well.

OTHER USES

Flowerheads may be dried for winter decoration.

This unassuming plant harbours great powers. 1 small leaf will speed decomposition of a wheelbarrow full of raw compost.

Infuse to make a copper fertilizer.

WARNING

Yarrow should always be taken in moderation and never for long periods because it may cause skin irritation. It should not be taken by pregnant women. Large doses produce headaches and vertigo.

MEDICINAL

Yarrow is one of the best known herbal remedies for fevers. Used as a hot infusion it will induce sweats that cools fevers and expels toxins. In China, yarrow is used fresh as a poultice for healing wounds. It can also be made into a decoction for wounds, chapped skin and rashes, and as a mouthwash for inflamed gums.

ALOE VERA

From the family Liliaceae/Aloëaceae

T here are between 250 and 350 species of aloe around the world. They are originally native to the arid areas of Southern Africa. In cultivation they need a frost-free environment. Aloe has been valued at least since the 4th century BC when Aristotle requested Alexander the Great to conquer Socotra in the Indian Ocean, where many species grow.

SPECIES

Aloe barbadensis
Aloe vera
Half-hardy perennial. Grown outside: ht 60cm (2ft), spread 60cm (2ft) or more. Grown as a house plant: ht 30cm (12in). Minimum temperature 10°C (50°F). Succulent grey/green pointed foliage, from which eventually grows a flowering stem with bell-shaped yellow or orange flowers.

Aloe arborescens 'Variegata'
Half-hardy perennial. Grown outside: ht, spread 2m (6ft). Minimum temperature 7°C (45°F). Each stem is crowned by rosettes of long, blue green leaves with toothed edges and cream stripes. Produces numerous spikes of red tubular flowers in late winter and spring.

Aloe variegata
Partridge-breasted aloe
Half-hardy perennial. A house plant only in temperate climates. Ht 30cm (12in), spread 10cm (4in). Minimum temperature 7°C (45°F). Triangular, white marked, dark green leaves. Spike of pinkish-red flowers in spring.

CULTIVATION

Propagation
Seed
A temperature of 21°C (70°F) must be maintained during germination. Sow onto the surface of a pot or tray and cover with Perlite. Place in a propagator with bottom heat. Germination is erratic – 4 to 24 months.

Division
In summer gently remove offshoots at the base of a mature plant. Leave for a day to dry, then pot into 2 parts compost to 1 part sharp sand mix. Water in and leave in warm place to establish. Give the parent plant a good liquid feed when returning to its pot.

Pest and Disease
Over watering causes it to rot off.

Maintenance
Spring: Give containerized plants a good dust! Spray the leaves with water. Give a good feed of liquid fertilizer.
Summer: Remove the basal offshoots of a mature plant to maintain the parent plant. Re-pot mature plants if necessary.
Autumn: Bring in pots if there is any danger of frost.
Winter: Rest all pot grown plants in a cool room (minimum temp 5°C (40°F); keep watering to the absolute minimum.

Garden Cultivation
Aloes enjoy a warm, frost-free position – full sun to partial shade – and a free-draining soil. Leave 1m (3ft) minimum between plants.

Harvest
Cut leaves throughout the growing season. A plant of more than 2 years has stronger properties.

CONTAINER GROWING

Compost must be gritty and well drained. Do not over water. Maintain a frost-free, light environment.

Aloe vera Aloe barbadensis

MEDICINAL

The gel obtained by breaking the leaves is a remarkable healer. Applied to wounds it forms a clear protective seal and encourages skin regeneration. It can be applied directly to cuts, burns, and is immediately soothing. Rumour has it that the US Government is building up stocks for use in the event of a nuclear disaster.

COSMETIC

Aloe vera is used in cosmetic preparations, in hand creams, suntan lotions and shampoos.

WARNING

It should be emphasized that, apart from external application, aloes are not for home medication. ALWAYS seek medical attention for serious burns.

Althaea officinalis

Marsh-Mallow

Also known as Mortification Root, Sweet Weed, Wymote, Marsh Mal-ice, Mesh-mellice, Wimote, and Althea. From the family Malvaceae.

Marsh-mallow is widely distributed from Western Europe to Siberia, from Australia to North America. It is common to find it in salt marshes and on banks near the sea.

The generic name, *Althaea*, comes from the Latin 'altheo' meaning 'I cure'. It may be the althea that Hippocrates recommended so highly for healing wounds. The Romans considered it a delicious vegetable, used it in barley soup and in stuffing for suckling pigs. In the Renaissance era the herbalists used marsh-mallow to cure sore throats, stomach trouble and toothache.

The soft, sweet marshmallow was originally flavoured with the root of marsh-mallow.

SPECIES

Althaea Officinalis
Marsh-Mallow
Hardy perennial. Ht 60-120cm (2-4ft), spread 60cm (2ft). Flowers pink or white in late summer/early autumn. Leaves, grey-green in colour, tear shaped and covered all over with soft hair.

CULTIVATION

Propagation
Seed
Sow in prepared seed or plug trays in the autumn.
Cover lightly with compost and winter outside under glass. Erratic germination takes place in spring. Plant out, 45cm (18in) apart, when large enough to handle.

Division
Divide established plants in the spring or autumn, replanting into a prepared site in the garden.

Pests and Diseases
This plant is usually free from pests and diseases.

Maintenance
Spring: Divide established plants.
Summer: Cut back after flowering for new growth.
Autumn: Sow seeds and winter the trays outside
Winter: No need for protection fully hardy.

Garden Cultivation
Marsh-mallow is highly attractive to butterflies. A good seaside plant, it likes a site in full sun with a moist or wet, moderately fertile soil. Cut back after flowering to encourage new leaves.

Harvest
Pick leaves for fresh use as required; they do not preserve well.
For use either fresh or dried, dig up the roots of 2-year-old plants in autumn, after the flowers and leaves have died back.

MEDICINAL

Due to its high mucilage content (35 percent in the root and 10 percent in the leaf), marsh-mallow soothes or cures inflammation, ulceration of the stomach and small intestine, soreness of throat, and pain from cystitis. An infusion of leaves or flowers serves as a soothing gargle; an infusion of the root can be used for coughs, diarrhoea and insomnia.
The pulverised roots may be used as a healing and drawing poultice, which should be applied warm.

CULINARY

Boil the roots to soften, then peel and quickly fry in butter.
Use the flowers in salads, and leaves, too, which may also be added to oil and vinegar, or steamed and served as a vegetable.

DECOCTION FOR DRY HANDS

Soak 25g (1oz) of scraped and finely chopped root in 150ml (¼pint; ⅔cup) of cold water for 24 hours. Strain well. Add 1 tablespoon of the decoction to 2 tablespoons of ground almonds, 1 teaspoon of milk and 1 teaspoon of cider vinegar. Beat it until well blended. Add a few drops of lavender oil. Put into a small screw top pot.

'I am sorry to say that Peter was not very well during the evening. His mother put him to bed and mad some chamomile tea and she gave a dose of it to Peter, one tablespoon full to be taken at bedtime.'
(*The Tale of Peter Rabbit* by Beatrix Potter)

Chamaemelum nobile

CHAMOMILE

From the family Compositae

Chamomile grows wild in Europe, North America, and many other countries. As a garden escapee, it can be found in pasture and other grassy places on sandy soils.

The generic name, *Chamaemelum*, is derived from the Greek *Khamaimelon*, meaning 'Earth Apple' or 'apple on the ground'.

Dyers Chamomile
Anthemis tinctora

SPECIES

Chamaemelum nobile
Roman Chamomile
Also known as Garden Chamomile, Ground Apple, Low Chamomile and Whig Plant
Hardy perennial evergreen. Ht 10cm (4in), spread 45cm (18in). White flowers with yellow centres all summer. Sweet smelling, finely divided foliage. Ideal for ground cover. Can be used as a lawn, but because it flowers it will need constant cutting.

Chamaemelum nobile 'Flore Pleno'
Double-flowered Chamomile
Hardy perennial evergreen. Ht 8cm (3in), spread 30cm (12in). Double white flowers all summer. Sweet-smelling, finely divided, thick foliage. Good for ground cover, in between paving stones and lawns. More compact habit than Roman Chamomile, and combines well with Chamomile Treneague.

Chamaemelum nobile 'Treneague' (**Anthemis nobile** 'Treneague')
Chamomile Treneague
Also known as Lawn Chamomile
Hardy perennial evergreen. Ht 6cm (2.5in), spread 15cm (6in). Non-flowering. Leaves are finely divided and very aromatic. Ideal for ground cover or mow-free lawn. Plant in well-drained soil, free from stones, 10-15cm (4-6in) apart.

Anthemis tinctora
Dyers Chamomile
Also known as Yellow Chamomile
Hardy perennial evergreen. Ht and spread 1m (3ft). Yellow daisy flowers in the summer. Leaves are mid-green and fern like. Principally a dye plant.

Matricaria recutita
German Chamomile
Also known as Scented Mayweed, Wild Chamomile
Hardy annual. Ht 60cm (24in), spread 10cm (4in). Scented white flowers with conical yellow centres from spring to early summer. Finely serrated aromatic foliage. The main use of this chamomile is medicinal.

CULTIVATION

Propagation
Seed
Dyers, Roman and German chamomiles can be grown from seed. Sow onto the surface of a prepared seed or plug tray. Use a bark, grit, peat compost. Cover with Perlite. Use bottom heat 19°C (65°F). Harden off and plant out or pot on.

Chamomile
Chamaemelum nobile

Cuttings
Double-flowered chamomile and Chamomile Treneague can only be propagated this way.
Take cuttings in the spring and autumn from the offsets or clusters of young shoots. They are easy to grow as they have aerial roots.

Division
All perennial chamomiles planted as specimen plants will benefit from being lifted in the spring of their second or third year and divided.

Pests and Diseases
As all the chamomiles are highly aromatic they are not troubled by pests or disease.

Maintenance
Spring. Collect offshoots, sow seeds. Fill in holes that have appeared in the chamomile lawn. Divide established plants. Give a liquid fertilizer feed to all established plants.
Summer. Water well. Do not allow to dry out. In the first season of a lawn, trim the plants to encourage bushing out and spreading. In late summer collect flowers from the Dyers chamomile and cut the plant back to

Dyers Chamomile
Anthemis tinctoria

6cm (2in) to promote new growth.
Autumn: Take cuttings. Divide if they have become too invasive. Cut back to promote new growth. Give the final feed of the season.
Winter: Only protect in extreme weather.

Garden Cultivation

All the chamomiles prefer a well-drained soil and a sunny situation, although they will adapt to most conditions.

As a lawn plant, chamomile gets more credit than it deserves. Chamomile lawns are infinitely less easy to maintain in good condition than grass lawns. There is no selective herbicide that will preserve chamomile and kill the rest of the weeds. It is a hands-and-knees job.

Prepare the site well, make sure the soil is light, slightly acid, and free from weeds and stones. Plant young plants in plug form. I use a mix of double-flowered and Treneague chamomile at a distance of 10-15cm (4-6in) apart. Keep all traffic off it for at least 12 weeks, and keep it to the minimum during the first year.

If all this seems daunting, compromise and plant a chamomile seat. Prepare the soil in the same way and do not sit on the seat for at least 12 weeks. Then sit down, smell the sweet aroma and sip a cool glass of wine. Summer is on hand . . .

Harvest

Leaves

Gather in spring and early summer for best results. Use fresh or dry.

Flowers

Pick when fully open, around mid-summer. Use fresh or dry. Dyers Chamomile flowers should be harvested in summer for their yellow dye.

COMPANION PLANTING

Chamomile has the unique name Physician's Plant because, when planted near ailing plants, it helps to revive them. Roman Chamomile can be planted next to onions to repel flying insects and improve the crop yield.

Chamomile Infusion

Bring 600ml (1 pint) water to the boil. Add a handful of chamomile leaves and flowers. Cover and let it stand for about half a day. Strain.

Spray it onto seedlings to prevent 'damping off'. If there is any liquid left pour it onto your compost heap. This acts like an activator for decomposition.

WARNING

When taken internally, excessive dosage can produce vomiting and vertigo.

CONTAINER GROWING

I would not advise growing chamomiles indoors, as they get very leggy, soft and prone to disease. But the flowers can look very cheerful in a sunny window box. Use Chamomile 'Flore Pleno', which has a lovely double flower head, or the non-flowering *C.* Treneague as an infill between bulbs, with a bark, grit, peat compost.

COSMETIC

Chamomile is used as a final rinse for fair hair to make it brighter. It should be poured over your hair several times. Pour 1 litre (1¾ pints) boiling water over one handful of chamomile flowers and steep for 30 minutes. Strain, cover and allow to cool.

MEDICINAL

German chamomile's highly scented dry flower heads contain up to 1 per cent of an aromatic oil that possesses powerful antiseptic and anti-inflammatory properties. Taken as a tea, it promotes gastric secretions and improves the appetite, while an infusion of the same strength can be used as an internal antiseptic. It may also be used as a douche or gargle for mouth ulcers and as an eye wash.

An oil for skin rashes or allergies can be made by tightly packing flower heads into a preserving jar, covering with olive oil and leaving in the sun for three weeks. If you suffer from overwrought nerves, add five or six drops of chamomile oil to the bath and this will help you relax at night.

Chamomile tea

1 heaped teaspoon chamomile flowers (dried or fresh)
1 teaspoon honey
slice of lemon (optional)

Put the chamomile flowers into a warm cup. Pour on boiling water. Cover and leave to infuse for 3–5 minutes. Strain and add the honey and lemon, if required. Can be drunk either hot or cold.

OTHER USES

Dyers Chamomile can be used as a dye plant. Depending on the mordant, its colour can vary from bright to olive/brown yellow.

German and Double-flowered Chamomile are best for herb pillows and pot pourri.

Cichorium intybus

CHICORY

Also known as Blue Endive, Bunks, Strip for Strip, Blue Sailors, Succory, Wild Chicory and Wild Succory. From the family Compositae.

Chicory
Cichorium intybus

Chicory grows throughout Europe in fields, hedgerows and on the roadside. In England and Wales it settles happily on lime-rich soils, although it is rarely found in Scotland and Ireland. In Australia and America it has been naturalized and is found on roadsides and field edges.

Chicory was an important medicinal herb, vegetable and salad plant in ancient Egypt, and in Greek and Roman times. Among the many delightful folk tales about the blue flowers, we hear that they are the transformed eyes of a lass weeping for her lover's ship, which never returned. Another from German folklore says that a young girl who could not stop weeping for her dead lover by the side of the road was turned into a flower called wegwort (chicory).

Careful English wives grew chicory among their herbs. It was good for purging and for the bladder. It was a principle of white magic that water distilled from the round blue flowers worked against inflammation and dimness of sight.

Chicory was grown in floral clocks because of the regular opening and closing of its flowers – they open to the sun and close about five hours later – and some gardeners, who have noticed that chicory leaves always align with North, credit the herb with metaphysical significance.

Since the 17th century, dried, roasted and ground roots of chicory have been used to make a drink. Two centuries later, Dickens described in his magazine *Household Words* the extensive cultivation of chicory in England as a coffee substitute.

Chicory leaves *Cichorium intybus*

Among the many varieties of chicory are:

Magdeburg or **Brunswick**
The best for producing roots which can be used as a coffee substitute.

Pain de Sucre (Sugar Loaf)
Looks like lettuce and can be used in the same way. Does not require blanching.

Red Verona
Crimson red foliage, good in salads.

Witloof (Brussels chicory)
This is the one grown for the chicons.

CULTIVATION

Propagation
Seeds
Sow the small seed thinly, either in spring or late summer in prepared pots, plug or seed trays, and cover with Perlite. For rapid germination (7-10 days), sow when freshest, in late summer. Winter the young plants under cover in a cold greenhouse, or on a cold windowsill. Plant these young plants out in the spring, 45cm (18in) apart. The seed can also be sown direct into the garden in spring.

SPECIES

Cichorium intybus
Chicory
Hardy perennial. Ht 1m (3ft), spread 30cm (1ft). Clear blue flowers from mid-summer to mid-autumn. Leaves mid-green, hairy underneath, and coarsely toothed.

Pests and Diseases
Fairly trouble free; watch for earwigs in the chicons.

Maintenance
Spring: Sow seed under protection for herb garden. Prepare site for outside sowing for chicons.
Summer: Sow seeds in situ for chicons.
Autumn: Dig up roots for forcing, also dig up and dry for coffee. Cut back flowers of plants in herb garden.
Winter: Dig in manure or compost where next year's chicon crop is to be grown.

Garden Cultivation
Seed

Grows easily. Sow in a sunny and open site with a light, preferably alkaline, soil. If you plan to harvest the roots prepare the site well, digging deeply. Thin the seedlings to 15-20cm (6-8in) distance apart in mid- to late summer. Transplant if necessary in the spring remembering that chicory grows fairly tall and looks well at the back of a border or against a fence, and needs to get the early morning sun as its flowers open at sunrise.

Harvest
Roots can be dug up throughout the summer, but are usually left until autumn. Lift the root. Shorten to 20cm (8in). Remove all side shoots and leaves, and stack in dry sand in the dark. Dry roots for coffee substitute.

Gather leaves when young for fresh use. Pick before flowering for drying. Collect flowers in early summer either fresh or to dry.

CONTAINER GROWING

As chicory grows so tall it is not ideally suited to container growing.

CHICONS

These are produced by forcing the roots in warmth and darkness, which blanches the new growth.

Prepare the soil, choosing a part of the garden that is rich in manure and well cultivated. Do not plant in recently manured land because this can cause forking in the roots.

In June sow the seeds. If you sow too early the plants may run to seed in the warm weather. Sow in 1cm (½in) drills, 30cm (12in) apart. Thin the seedlings.

Keep area well watered in dry weather and weed free.

In late autumn, early winter carefully begin to dig up a few roots for forcing. Cut off the tops just above the crown. Plant the roots close together in a box of loamy soil with the crowns of the roots at soil level. Water and cover with another box. These chicons must remain in total darkness if they are not to become bitter. Put the box where the temperature does not go below 10°C (50°F).

In 4-6 weeks the chicons will be 15-20cm (6-8in) long and ready to harvest. If you break the chicons off carefully, instead of cutting, a second crop will appear. They will be smaller and looser but just as tasty.

The whole process can be repeated. When the remaining plants have died back dig up the roots, trim, and store in sand in a frost-proof room, and force as required. One word of warning: do not pick the chicons before you need them because even after an hour in the light they will become limp.

WARNING

Excessive and continued use may impair the function of the retina.

Chicory in salad

MEDICINAL

Chicory, like dandelion, is a gentle but effective, bitter tonic, which increases the flow of bile. It is also a specific remedy for gall stones, and for this reason Galen called it 'friend of the liver'. Like dandelion it has diuretic properties and can be used for treating rheumatism and gout, because it eliminates uric acid from the body.

The roots, in the form of syrup or succory, make an excellent laxative for children.

OTHER USES

Boil the leaves to produce a blue dye.

Grow crop for animal fodder.

CULINARY

Add young leaves and flowers to summer salads, use forced leaves as a winter salad. Toss chicons in salads, or braise in butter as a vegetable dish.

Roasted chicory roots are still widely used as an excellent substitute or adulterant for coffee. Wash, slice and dry in gentle heat. Roast and grind.

When young the root can be dug up, boiled and served with a sauce.

Digitalis purpurea

FOXGLOVE

Also known as Digitalis 'American' Foxglove, Deadmen's Bells, Dogs Fingers, Fairy Fingers, Fairy Gloves, Fringe Flower, Folksglove, Lion Mouths, Ladiesglove, Purple Foxgloves, Witch's Glove, Fairy Glove, Gloves of Our Lady, Bloody Fingers, Fairy Caps and Fairy Thimbles. From the family Scrophulariaceae.

Foxglove grows throughout Europe and is a common wild flower in temperate climates throughout the world, seeding freely in woods and hedgerows.

The principal common name probably derives from the Anglo-Saxon 'foxglue' or 'foxmusic', after the shape of a musical instrument. Judging by its other names it would seem that it was also thought to be a fairy's plant or a goblin's plant, at least in England. Its appearance – its height, the glove shape of the corolla, and the poison of its leaves – seems somehow to beg for its own folklore.

In 1542, Fuchs called it *Digitalis* after the finger-like shape of its flowers but he considered it a violent medicine and it was not until the late 18th century that William Withering used foxglove tea in Shropshire for dropsy that its reputation as a medicinal herb grew. Commercial production of digitalis now takes place mainly in south-east Europe.

SPECIES

There are many extremely attractive species and cultivars. One of the national collections is held by The Botanic Nursery, Atworth, in Wiltshire.

Digitalis grandiflora (Digitalis ambigua)
Yellow Foxglove
Hardy evergreen perennial. Ht 75cm (30in), spread 30cm (12in). Creamy yellow, downward pointing, tubular flowers all summer. Smooth, strongly veined leaves.

Digitalis purpurea
Foxglove (wild, common)
Shortlived perennial, grown as a biennial. Ht 1-1.5m (3-5ft), spread 60cm (2ft). Flowers all shades of pink, purple and red in summer. Rough, mid- to dark green leaves.

Digitalis purpurea alba
White Foxglove
Shortlived perennial, grown as a biennial. Ht 1-1.5m (3-5ft), spread 30-45cm (12-18in). Tubular white flowers all summer. Rough, mid- to dark green leaves.

Foxglove *Digitalis purpurea*

WARNING

Foxgloves are poisonous and should not be eaten or used domestically. Even touching the plant has been known to cause rashes, headaches and nausea. DO NOT USE without medical direction.

White Foxglove *Digitalis purpurea alba*

If you live in a cold climate -10°C (14°F) protect during the first winter. Use agricultural fleece, straw, bracken or pine needles. In areas where the soil is damp and cold, it is advisable to lift the plants for the first winter and keep them in a cold frame, replanting the following spring.

Harvest
This is not advised unless you are a herbalist or a pharmacist.

MEDICINAL

Foxgloves are grown commercially for the production of a drug the discovery (a major medical breakthrough) of which is a classic example of a productive marriage between folklore and scientific curiosity. Foxgloves contain glycosides which are extracted from second-year leaves to make the heart drug digitalis. For more than 200 years digitalis has provided the main drug for treating heart failure. It is also a powerful diuretic. Although a synthetic form of the drug has been developed, the plant is still grown commercially for the drug industry.

CULTIVATION

Propagation
The seed is very small and fine. Sow in either spring or autumn as carefully as possible, using the cardboard method, either directly onto the prepared ground, or into pots or plug trays. Sow on the surface; do not cover with Perlite, but with a piece of glass, which should be removed as soon as the seedlings appear. No bottom heat required.

Remember, they will not flower the first season.

Pests and Diseases
Foxgloves, on the whole, are pest and disease free.

Maintenance
Spring: Sow seeds. Plant out first-year plants.
Summer: Remove main flowering shoot after flowering.
Autumn: Check round second-year plants for self-sown seedlings, thin out if over-crowded, remove if not required. Pot up a few in case of an exceptionally hard winter.
Winter: In the majority of cases no protection needed.

See Garden Cultivation for the exceptions.

Garden Cultivation
This is one of the most poisonous plants in the flora. Foxgloves will grow in most conditions, even dry exposed sites, but do best in semi-shade and a moist but well-drained acid soil enriched with leaf mould. The rosettes and leaves are formed the first year and the flower spike the second. The plant then dies but usually leaves lots of self-sown babies nearby. Water well in dry weather and remove the centre spike after flowering to increase the size of the flowers on the side shoots.

CONTAINER GROWING

These tall elegant plants do not honestly suit growing in containers. It is possible, but care has to be taken that the plant is not damaged in winds. Use a soil-based compost. Water regularly.

Filipendula

MEADOWSWEET

***Also known as Bridewort, Meadow Queen, Meadow-Wort, and
Queen of the Meadow. From the family Rosaceae.***

Meadowsweet can be found growing wild in profusion near streams
and rivers, in damp meadows, fens and marshlands, or wet woodlands
to 1,000m/3,300ft altitude.

It is a native of Europe and Asia that has been successfully introduced into,
and is naturalized in, North America.

The generic name, *Filipendula,* comes from 'filum', meaning thread, 'pendulus',
meaning hanging. This is said to describe the root tubers that hang,
characteristically of the genus, on fibrous roots.

The common name, meadowsweet, is said to be derived from the
Anglo-Saxon word 'medesweete', which itself owes its origin to the fact that
the plant was used to flavour mead, a drink made from fermented honey.

It has been known by many other names. In Chaucer's *The Knight's Tale* it
is Meadwort and was one of the ingredients in a drink called 'save'. It was also
known as Bridewort, because it was strewn in churches for festivals and
weddings and made into bridal garlands. In Europe it took its name Queen of
the Meadow from the way the herb can dominate a low-lying, damp meadow.
In America, it became Gravelroot or Joe Pie Weed (*Eupatorium purpureum*).

In the 16th century, when it was customary to strew floors with rushes and herbs (both to
give warmth underfoot and to overcome smells and infections), it was a favourite of Queen
Elizabeth I. She desired it above all other herbs in her chambers.

The sap contains a chemical of the same group as salicylic acid, an ingredient of aspirin. It
was isolated for the first time in the 19th century by an Italian professor. When the drug
company Bayer formulated acetylsalicylic acid, they called it aspirin after the old botanical
name for meadowsweet, *Spirea ulmaria.*

SPECIES

Filipendula ulmaria
Meadowsweet
Hardy perennial. Ht 60-
120cm (2-4ft), spread 60cm
(2ft). Clusters of creamy-
white flowers in mid-
summer. Green leaf made
up of up to 5 pairs of big
leaflets separated by pairs of
smaller leaflets.

Filipendula ulmaria Aurea
Golden Meadowsweet
Hardy perennial. Ht and
spread 30cm (12in). Clusters
of creamy-white flowers in
mid-summer. Bright golden
yellow, divided leaves in
spring that turn a lime
colour in summer.
Susceptible to sun scorch.

**Filipendula ulmaria
'Variegata'**
Variegated Meadowsweet
Hardy perennial. Ht 45cm
(18in) and spread 30cm
(12in). Clusters of creamy-
white flowers in mid-
summer. Divided leaf,
dramatically variegated
green and yellow in spring.
Fades a bit as the season
progresses.

**Filipendula vulgaris
(hexapetala)**
Dropwort
Hardy perennial. Ht 60-
90cm (2-3ft), spread 45cm
(18in). Summertime clusters
of white flowers (larger than
meadowsweet). Fern-like
green leaves.

CULTIVATION

Propagation

Seed

Sow in prepared seed or plug trays in the autumn. Cover lightly with compost (not Perlite) and winter outside under glass. Check from time to time that the compost has not become dry as this will inhibit germination. Stratification is helpful but not essential. Germination should take place in spring. When the seedlings are large enough to handle, plant out, 30cm (12in) apart, into a prepared site.

Division

The golden and variegated forms are best propagated by division. This is easily done in the autumn. Dig up established plant and tease the plantlets apart; they separate easily. Either replant in a prepared site, 30cm (12in) apart, or, if it is 1 of the decorative varieties, pot up using the bark, peat mix of compost.

Pests and Diseases

Meadowsweet rarely suffers from these.

Maintenance

Spring: Sow seeds if required.
Summer: Cut back after flowering.
Autumn: Divide established plants, sow seed for wintering outside.
Winter: No need for protection.

Garden Cultivation

Meadowsweet adapts well to the garden, but does prefer sun/semi-shade and a moisture retentive soil. If your soil is free-draining, mix in plenty of well-rotted manure and/or leaf mould, and plant in semi-shade.

Harvest

Gather young leaves for fresh or dry use before flowers appear. Pick flowers just as they open and use fresh or dry.

MEDICINAL

The whole plant is a traditional remedy for an acidic stomach.

The fresh root is used in homeopathic preparations and is effective on its own in the treatment of diarrhoea.

The flowers, when made into a tea, are a comfort to flu victims.

Golden Meadowsweet
Filipendula ulmaria Aurea

CULINARY

A charming, local vet who made all kinds of vinegars and pickles gave me to try meadowsweet vinegar. Much to my amazement it was lovely, and combined well with oil to make a different salad dressing, great when used with a flower salad.

I am not a fan of meadowsweet flower fritters so mention them only in passing. The flowers do however make a very good wine, and add flavour to meads and beers. The flowers can also be added to stewed fruit and jams, introducing a subtle almond flavour.

Young leaves can be added to soups, but are not recommended for the faint-hearted!

OTHER USES

A black dye can be obtained from the roots by using a copper mordant.

Use dried leaves and flowers in potpourris.

CONTAINER GROWING

Golden and variegated meadowsweet look very attractive in containers, but make sure the compost retains moisture. Position in partial shade to inhibit drying out and prevent sun scorch. The plant dies back in winter so leave it outside in a place where the natural weathers can reach it. If you live in an extremely cold area, protect the container from damage by placing in a site protected from continuous frost, but not warm. Liquid feed only twice during flowering, following manufacturer's instructions.

Meadowsweet dye

Meadowsweet *Filipendula ulmaria*

'So Gladiators fierce and rude,
Mingled it with their daily food,
And he who battled down subdued,
A wreath of Fennel wore.'
Henry Wadsworth Longfellow (1807-82)

Foeniculum vulgare

FENNEL

Also known as Large Fennel, Sweet Fennel and Wild Fennel. From the family Umbelliferae.

It grows wild in Europe and in most temperate countries and is naturalized in the western USA. The generic name, Foeniculum, derives from the Latin 'foenum' which means 'hay', and refers to the foliar structure.

The ancient Greeks thought very highly of fennel and used it as a slimming aid and for treating more than twenty different illnesses. It was also much valued by the Romans in an age of banquets. They ate its leaf, root and seed in salads, and baked it in bread and cakes. Warriors took fennel to keep in good health, while Roman ladies ate it to prevent obesity. In Anglo-Saxon times it was used on fasting days presumably because, as the Greeks had already discovered, it stills pangs of hunger. And more recently, in American Puritan communities, it became known as the Meeting Seeds, because seeds of fennel and dill were taken to church to allay hunger during long services.

In the Middle Ages, fennel was a favourite stewing herb, for not only is it fragrant and flavoursome, it also keeps insects at bay and was used in the kitchen to protect and lend flavour to food which was often far from fresh so making it palatable. In the 16th century Gerard praised it as an aid to eyesight and Culpeper for poison by snakebite or mushrooms.

Foeniculum vulgare
Fennel
Also known as Garden Fennel, Common Fennel, and Green Fennel. Hardy perennial. Ht 1.5m-2.1m (4-7ft), spread 45cm (18in). Lots of small yellow flowers in large umbels in late summer. Soft green feathery foliage.

Foeniculum vulgare purpureum
Bronze Fennel
As **F. vulgare** Very striking bronze feathery leaves.

Foeniculum vulgare var. dulce
Florence Fennel
Also known as Finocchio
Grown as an annual. Ht 75cm-1m (2.5-3ft). Clusters of small yellow flowers in late summer. Leaf feathery and green. The base develops to form a white bulbous sweet vegetable, with a crisp texture and a delicate aniseed flavour.

CULTIVATION

Propagation
Seeds
Sow all varieties early in spring in prepared pots or plug trays, and cover with Perlite.
Bottom heat of 15-21°C (60-70°F) will speed germination. When large enough to handle plant out.

Roots
Division is only really successful if you have a light sandy soil, when roots will divide easily. This should be done in the autumn.

Bronze Fennel *Foeniculum vulg purpureum*

Garden Cultivation

Fennel likes a sunny position in fertile, well-drained, loamy soil. Add an extra layer of sharp sand in the drill on a clay soil. Sow the seed after any frosts, thinning to 50cm (20in) apart. Do not grow fennel near dill or coriander as cross pollination will reduce fennel's seed production.

Fennel grown in a hot dry spot produces a sparse clump, 1.2-1.5m (4-5ft) high, with very thin, highly aromatic leaves. In a decent garden soil, fennel looks more like a dome of green or purple candyfloss.

Even though fennel is perennial, after three years it should be replaced.

Florence Fennel is grown only from seed. Sow in shallow trenches during the early summer in a rich well-composted soil for the bulbous roots to reach maturity by autumn. Thin out to 20cm (9in) apart.

During dry spells water well. When the root swelling is the size of a golf ball, blanch it by drawing some soil around it. After 2-3 weeks, when the size of a tennis ball, harvest.

Pests and Diseases

When the plants are very young root rot may occur if over watered. Green fly may also occasionally infest the plant. This can be treated with horticultural soap.

Maintenance

Spring: Sow seed of all varieties.
Summer: Pick flowering heads to maintain leaf production.
Autumn: Sow seeds in trays and force with heat for use in winter salads.
Winter: Cut back old growth, tidy up round established plants. Fennel will die back into the ground in winter. No need to protect unless temperatures fall below -10°C (14°F).

Harvest

Pick young stems and leaves as required. Freeze leaves or infuse in oil or vinegar.

Collect ripe seeds for sowing or to dry for culinary use. Dig up Florence Fennel bulbs when sufficiently mature and as required

COMPANION PLANTING

Fennel attracts hoverflies so helps keep whitefly at bay.

CONTAINER GROWING

The bronze variety looks especially attractive. Use the bark, grit, peat mix of compost. It may need staking when in flower. In the summer shelter from midday sun, water and feed regularly. Repot each year to maintain health.

OTHER USES

Seed and leaf can be used in facial steams and in baths for deep cleansing. A facial pack made of fennel tea and honey is good for wrinkles.

Finally, a yellow dye substance can be extracted.

MEDICINAL

To make fennel tea put a teaspoon of seeds in a tea cup, add boiling water, cover for 5 minutes, then strain and drink to aid digestion or prevent both heartburn or constipation. A teaspoon of this cooled tea is good for babies with colic. Steep a compress in the tea and place on the eyelid, to ease inflammation or watery eye, or let the solution cool and bathe the naked eye.

Warning: Taken in large doses, the essence can cause convulsions and disturb the nervous system.

Trout with Fennel

CULINARY

Fennel is an additional seasoning for fat meats like pork and stuffings for poultry and lamb. It is as delicious as a salad or vegetable dressing.

Use seeds in sauces, fish dishes and bread; leaves finely chopped over salads and cooked vegetables, and in soups and stuffing for oily fish; and young stems to add an extra crunch to salads.

The bulb of Florence Fennel can be cooked as a root vegetable or sliced or grated raw into sandwiches or salads.

Fish with Fennel
Serves 4

Whole fish – trout, mackerel, mullet (4 fish, 500g/1lb each)
1 cup of fresh sprigs of fennel
1 tablespoon cooking oil
Brandy

Clean the fish and fill with sprigs of chopped green fennel leaves. With a sharp knife score the fish on each side and brush with oil. Season lightly with salt and pepper. Arrange bed of fennel sticks on base of a greased oven-proof dish. Carefully place fish on the sticks and cook in a hot oven

(450°F/230°C/Gas Mark 8) for 15 minutes.

To serve: transfer fennel sticks and fish onto a flat fire proof serving dish. Warm the brandy and pour over the fish and set alight. The fennel will burn and the whole dish becomes deliciously aromatic.

Finocchio Salad (with Florence Fennel)
Serves 2

2 medium-sized fennel bulbs
12 black olives
125g/5oz carton plain yoghurt
1 small lettuce
Juice of 1 lemon, Chopped parsley

Trim the fennel bulbs and wash carefully. Cut into thin slices. Mix with yoghurt, lemon juice and olives. Arrange the mixture decoratively on a bed of lettuce leaves. Garnish with slices of lemon and chopped parsley.

Humulus lupulus

HOPS

Also known as Hopbind and Hop vine. From the family Cannabaceae.

Native of the Northern temperate zones, cultivated commercially, especially in Northern Europe, North America and Chile.

Roman records from the 1st century AD describe hops as a popular garden plant and vegetable, the young shoots being sold in markets to be eaten rather like asparagus. Hop gardens did not become widespread in Europe until the 9th century. In Britain the hop was a wild plant and used as a vegetable before it became one of the ingredients of beer. It was not until the 16th century that the word hop and the practice of flavouring and preserving beer with the strobiles or female flowers of the *Humulus lupulus* were introduced into Britain by Flemish immigrants, and replaced traditional bitter herbs such as alehoof and alecost.

During the reign of Henry VIII, Parliament was petitioned against the use of the hop, as it was said that it was a wicked weed that would spoil the taste of the drink, ale, and endanger the people. Needless to say the petition was thrown out. The use of hops revolutionized brewing since it enabled beer to be kept for longer.

Hops have also been used as medicine for at least as long as for brewing. The flowers are famous for their sedative effect and were either drunk as a tea or stuffed in a hop pillow to sleep on.

Common Hop
Humulus lupulus

Golden Hop
Humulus lupulus
'Aureus'

Humulus lupulus
Common Hop
Hardy perennial, a herbaceous climber. Ht up to 6m (20ft). There are separate female and male plants. The male plant has yellowish flowers growing in branched clusters. They are without sepals and have 5 tepals and 5 stamen. The female plant has tiny greenish yellow, scented flowers, hidden by big scales. The scales become papery when the fruiting heads are ripe. These are the flowers that are harvested for beer. The mid-green leaves have 3 to 5 lobes with sharply toothed edges. The stems are hollow, and are covered with tiny hooked prickles. These enable the plant to cling to shrubs, trees, or anything else. It always entwines clockwise.

Humulus lupulus 'Aureus'
Golden Hop
Hardy perennial, a herbaceous climber. Ht up to 6m (20ft), The main difference between this plant and the common hop is that the leaves and flowers are much more golden, which makes it very attractive in the garden and in dried flower arrangements. It has the same properties as the common hop.

Common Hop *Humulus lupulus*

CULTIVATION

Propagation
Seed

Beer is made from the un-pollinated female flowers. If you grow from seed you will not know the gender for 2 to 3 years, which is the time it takes before good flowers are produced. Obtain seed from specialist seedsmen.

Sow in summer or autumn. The seed is on the medium to large size so sow sparingly; if using plug trays, 1 per cell. Push the seed into and cover it with the compost. Then cover the tray with a sheet of glass or polythene, and leave somewhere cool to germinate – a cold frame, a cold glasshouse, or a garage. Germination can be very erratic. If the seed is not fresh you may need to give the hot/cold treatment.

Warning: As the seed will be from wild hops these should not be grown in areas of commercial hop growing, because they might contaminate the crop.

Cuttings

Softwood cuttings should be taken in spring or early summer from the female plant. Choose young shoots and take the cuttings in the morning as they will loose water very fast and wilt.

Division

In the spring dig up and divide the root stems and suckers of established plants. Replant 1m (3ft) apart against support.

Pests and Diseases

The most common disease is hop wilt. If this occurs, dig up and burn. Do not plant hops in that area again.

Leaf miner can sometimes be a problem. Remove infected leaves immediately.

The golden variety sometimes suffers from sun scorch. If this occurs prune

to new growth, and change its position if possible the following season.

Maintenance

Spring: Divide roots and separate rooted stems and suckers in spring. Re-pot container grown plants. Check trellising.
Summer: Sow seed late in the season.
Autumn: Cut back remaining growth into the ground. Give the plants a good feed of manure or compost. Bring containers into a cool place.
Winter: No need for protection.

Garden Cultivation

For successful plants the site should be sunny and open, the soil needs to be rich in humus and dug deeply. It is not generally necessary to tie the plants if good support is at hand. A word of warning, you must dominate the plant. Certainly it will need thinning and encouraging to entwine where you want it to go rather than where it chooses. But remember that it dies back completely in winter. Cut the plant into the ground each autumn and then give it a good feed of manure or compost.

Harvest

Pick young fresh sideshoots in spring. Gather young fresh leaves as required.

Pick male flowers as required. Pick ripe female flowers in early autumn. Dry and use within a few months, otherwise the flavour becomes unpleasant.

CONTAINER GROWING

Hops, especially the golden variety, can look very attractive in a large container with something to grow up. Use a compost made up of the bark, peat

mix, and feed regularly with a liquid fertilizer from late spring to mid-summer. Keep well watered in the summer months and fairly dry in winter. It can be grown indoors in a position with good light such as a conservatory, but it seldom flowers. Provide some form of shade during sunny periods. During the winter months, make sure it has a rest by putting the pot in a cool place, keeping the compost on the dry side. Re-pot each year.

OTHER USES

The leaf can be used to make a brown dye. If you live close to a brewery it is worth chatting them up each autumn for the spent hops, which makes either a great mulch or a layer in a compost heap.

WARNING

Contact dermatitis can be caused by the pollen of the female flower. Also, hops are not recommended in the treatment of depressive illnesses because of their sedative effect.

MEDICINAL

Hop tea made from the female flower only is recommended for nervous diarrhoea, insomnia and restlessness. It also helps to stimulate appetite, dispel flatulence and relieve intestinal cramps. A cold tea taken an hour before meals

Hop pillow

is particularly good for digestion.

It can be useful combined with fragrant valerian for coughs and nervous spasmodic conditions. Recent research into hops has shown that it contains a certain hormone, which accounts for the beneficial effect of helping mothers improve their milk flow.

To make a hop pillow, sprinkle hops with alcohol and fill a small bag or pillowcase with them (which all in all is bound to knock you out).

CULINARY

In early spring pick the young side shoots, steam them (or lightly boil), and eat like asparagus. The male flowers can be parboiled, cooled and tossed into salads. The young leaves can be quickly blanched to remove any bitterness and added to soups or salads.

Hypericum perforatum

ST JOHN'S WORT

Also known as Warriors Wound, Amber, Touch and Heal, Grace of God and Herb of St John. From the family Guttiferae.

This magical herb is found in temperate zones of the world in open situations on semi-dry soils.

Whoever treads on St John's Wort after sunset will be swept up on the back of a magic horse that will charge round the heavens until sunrise before depositing its exhausted rider on the ground.

Besides its magical attributes, *Hypericum* has medicinal properties and was universally known as the 'Grace of God'. In England it cured mania, in Russia it gave protection against hydrophobia and the Brazilians knew it as an antidote to snake bite. St John's Wort ('wort', incidentally, is Anglo-Saxon for 'medicinal herb') has been used to raise ghosts and exorcise spirits. When crushed, the leaves release a balsamic odour similar to incense, which was said to be strong enough to drive away evil sprits. The red pigment from the crushed flowers was taken to signify the blood of St John at his beheading, for the herb is in full flower on 24th June, St John's Day.

Division
Divide established plants in the autumn.

Pests and Diseases
Largely free from pests and diseases.

Maintenance
Spring: Sow seeds.
Summer: Cut back after flowering to stop self-seeding.
Autumn: Divide established clumps.
Winter: No need for protection, fully hardy.

Garden Cultivation
Tolerates most soils, in sun or light shade, but it can be invasive in light soils.

Harvest
Harvest leaves and flowers as required.

OTHER USES

The flowers release a yellow dye with alum, and a red dye with alcohol.

WARNING

St John's Wort has sometimes poisoned livestock. Its use also makes the skin sensitive to light.

MEDICINAL

Oil extracted by macerating the flowers in vegetable oil and applied externally eases neuralgia and the pain of sciatica wounds, varicose veins, ulcers and sunburn. Only take internally under supervision.

SPECIES

Hypericum perforatum
St John's Wort
Hardy perennial. Ht 30-90cm (12-36in), spread 30cm (12in). Scented yellow flowers with black dots in summer. The small leaves are stalkless; covered with tiny perforations (hence **perforatum**), which are in fact translucent glands. This is the magical species.

CULTIVATION

Propagation
Seed
Sow very small seed in spring into prepared seed or plug trays, and cover with Perlite. Germination is usually in 10-20 days depending on the weather. When the seedlings are large enough to handle and after a period of hardening off, plant out 30cm (12in) apart.

CONTAINER GROWING

Can be grown in containers, but it is a bit tall so you do need a large clump for it to look effective. Use a soil based compost. Water in the summer months; only feed with liquid fertilizer twice during the growing season, otherwise it produces more leaf than flower.

Marrubium vulgare

WHITE HOREHOUND

Also known as Horehound and Maribeum. From the family Labiatae.

Common throughout Europe and America, the plant grows wild everywhere from coastal to mountainous areas.

The botanical name comes from the Hebrew 'marrob' which translates as 'bitter juice'. The common name is derived from the old English 'har hune' meaning a downy plant.

SPECIES

Marrubium vulgare
White Horehound
Hardy perennial. Ht 45cm (18in), spread 30cm (12in). Small clusters of white flowers from the second year in midsummer. The leaves are green and wrinkled with an underside of a silver woolly texture. There is also a variegated version.

CULTIVATION

Propagation
Seed
The fairly small seed should be sown in early spring in a seed or plug tray, using the bark, grit, peat mix of compost. Germination takes 2-3 weeks. Prick out into pots or transplant to the garden after a period of hardening off.

Cuttings
Softwood cuttings taken from the new growth in summer usually root within 3-4 weeks. Use the bark, grit, peat mix of compost. Winter under protection in a cold frame or cold greenhouse.

Division
Established clumps benefit from division in the spring.

Pests and Diseases
If it is very wet and cold in winter, the plant can rot off.

Maintenance
Spring: Divide established clumps. Prune new growth to maintain shape. Sow seed.
Summer: Trim after flowering to stop the plant flopping and prevent self-seeding. Take cuttings.
Autumn: Divide only if it has dangerously transgressed its limits.
Winter: Protect only if season excessively wet.

Garden Cultivation
White horehound grows best in well-drained, dryish soil, biased to alkaline, sunny and protected from high winds. Seed can be sown direct into a prepared garden in late spring, once the soil has started to warm up. Thin the seedlings to 30cm (12in) distance apart.

Harvest
The leaves and flowering tops are gathered in the spring, just as the plants come into flower, when the essential oil is at its richest. Use fresh or dried.

CONTAINER GROWING

Horehound can be grown in a large container situated in a sunny position. Use a compost which drains well and do not overwater. Only feed after flowering otherwise it produces lush growth which is too soft.

OTHER USES

Infuse the leaf as a spray for cankerworm in trees.
Mix the infusion with milk and put in a dish as a fly killer. Do not spray!

MEDICINAL

White horehound is still extensively used in cough medicine, and for calming a nervous heart; its property, marrubiin, in small amounts, normalizes an irregular heart beat. The plant has also been used to reduce fevers and treat malaria.

A Cold Cure
Finely chop 9 small horehound leaves. Mix 1 tablespoon of honey and eat slowly to ease sore throat or cough. Repeat several times if necessary.

Cough Sweets

100g/4oz of fresh white horehound leaves
½ teaspoon of crushed aniseed
3 crushed cardamom seeds

Put into 600ml/1pint of water and simmer for 20 minutes. Strain through a filter. Over a low heat, dissolve 350g/12oz of white sugar and 350g/12oz of moist brown sugar in the liquid and boil over a medium heat until the syrup hardens when drops are put into cold water. Pour into an oiled tray. Score when partially cooled. Store in wax paper.

Horehound sweets

Melissa officinalis

LEMON BALM

Also known as Balm, Melissa, Balm Mint, Bee Balm, Blue Balm, Cure All, Dropsy Plant, Garden Balm and Sweet Balm. From the family Labiatae.

This plant is a native of the Mediterranean region and Central Europe. It is now naturalized in North America and as a garden escapee in Britain.

This ancient herb was dedicated to the goddess Diana, and used medicinally by the Greeks some 2,000 years ago. The generic name, *Melissa*, comes from the Greek word for bee and the Greek belief that if you put sprigs of balm in an empty hive it would attract a swarm; equally, if planted nearby bees in residence in a hive they would never go away. This belief was still prevalent in medieval times when sugar was highly priced and honey a luxury.

In the Middle Ages lemon balm was used to soothe tension, to dress wounds, as a cure for toothache, mad dog bites, skin eruptions, crooked necks, and sickness during pregnancy. It was even said to prevent baldness, and ladies made linen or silk amulets filled with lemon balm as a lucky love charm.

It has been acclaimed the world over for promoting long life. Prince Llewellyn of Glamorgan drank Melissa tea, so he claimed, every day of the 108 years of his life.

Wild claims apart, as a tonic for melancholy it has been praised by herbal writers for centuries and is still used today in aromatherapy to counter depression.

Melissa officinalis
Lemon Balm
Hardy perennial. Ht 75cm (30in), spread 45cm (18in) or more. Clusters of small, pale yellow/white flowers in summer. The green leaves are oval toothed, slightly wrinkled, and highly aromatic when crushed.

Melissa officinalis 'All Gold'
Golden Lemon Balm
Half-hardy perennial. Ht 60cm (24in), spread 30cm (12in) or more. Clusters of small, pale yellow/white flowers in summer. The leaves are all yellow, oval in shape, toothed, slightly wrinkled and aromatic with a lemon scent when crushed. The leaves are prone to scorching in high summer; also more tender than the other varieties.

left: **Lemon balm** *Melissa officinalis* and **Variegated Lemon Balm** *Melissa officinalis 'Aurea'*

Melissa officinalis 'Aurea'
Variegated Lemon Balm
Hardy perennial. Ht 60cm (24in), spread 30cm (12in) or more. Clusters of small, pale yellow/white flowers in summer. The green/gold variegated leaves are oval, toothed, slightly wrinkled and aromatic with a lemon scent when crushed. This variety is as hardy as common lemon balm. The 1 problem is that in high season it reverts to green. To maintain variegation keep cutting back, this in turn will promote new growth which should be variegated.

Lemon balm *Melissa officinalis* **in flower**

left: **Variegated Lemon Balm** *Melissa officinalis 'Aurea'*

CULTIVATION

Propagation
Seed
Common Lemon Balm can be grown from seed. The seed is small but manageable, and it is better to start it off under protection. Sow in prepared seed or plug trays in early spring, using the bark, grit, peat mix of compost and cover with Perlite. Germination takes between 10 and 14 days. The seeds dislike being wet so, after the initial watering, try not to water again until germination starts. When seedlings are large enough to handle, prick out and plant in the garden, 45cm (18in) apart.

Cuttings
The variegated and golden lemon balm can only be propagated by cuttings or division. Take softwood cuttings from the new growth in late spring/early summer. As the cutting material will be very soft take extra care when collecting it.

Division
The root stock is compact but easy to divide (autumn or spring). Replant directly into the garden in a prepared site.

Pests and Diseases
The only problem likely to affect lemon balm is a form of the rust virus; cut the plant back to the ground, dispose of all the infected leaves, including any that may have accidentally fallen on the ground.

Maintenance
Spring: Sow seeds. Divide established plants.
Summer: Keep trimming established plants. Cut back after flowering to help prevent self-seeding.
Autumn: Divide established plants, or any that may have encroached on other plant areas.
Winter: Protect plants if the temperature falls below -5°C (23°F). The plant dies back, leaving but a small presence on the surface of the soil. Protect with a bark or straw mulch or agricultural fleece.

Garden Cultivation
Lemon Balm will grow in almost any soil and in any position. It does prefers a fairly rich, moist soil in sunny position with some midday shade. Keep all plants trimmed around the edges to restrict growth and encourage fresh shoots. In the right soil conditions this can be a very invasive plant. Unlike horseradish, the established roots are not difficult to uproot if things get out of hand.

Harvesting
Pick leaves throughout the summer for fresh use. For drying, pick just before the flowers begin to open when flavour is best; handle gently to avoid bruising. The aroma is rapidly lost, together with much of its therapeutic value, when dried or stored.

CULINARY

Lemon Balm is one of those herbs that smells delicious but tastes like school-boiled cabbage water when cooked.
  Add fresh leaves to vinegar. Add leaves to wine cups, teas and beers, or use chopped with fish and mushroom dishes. Mix freshly chopped with soft cheeses.
  It has frequently been incorporated in proprietary cordials for liqueurs and its popularity in France led to its name 'Tea de France'.
  It is used as a flavouring for certain cheeses in parts of Switzerland.

Lemon balm with cream cheese

MEDICINAL

Lemon Balm tea is said to relieve headaches and tension and to restore the memory. It is also good to drink after meals to ease the digestion, flatulence and colic. Use fresh or frozen leaves in infusions because the volatile oil tends to disappear during the drying process.
  The isolated oil used in aromatherapy is recommended for nervousness, depression, insomnia and nervous headaches. It also helps eczema sufferers.

OTHER USES
This is a most useful plant to keep bees happy. The flower may look boring to you but it is sheer heaven to them. So plant lemon balm around beehives or orchards to attract pollinating bees.

CONTAINER GROWING

If you live in an area that suffers from very cold winters, the gold form would benefit from being grown in containers. This method suits those with a small garden who do not want a takeover bid from lemon balm. Use the bark, peat, grit mix of compost. Only feed with liquid fertilizer in the summer, otherwise the growth will become too lush and soft, and aroma and colour diminished. Water normally throughout the growing season. Allow the container to become very dry (but not totally) in winter, and keep the pots in a cool, protected environment.

Oenothera

EVENING PRIMROSE

Also known as Common Evening Primrose, Evening Star, Fever Plant, Field Primrose, King's Cure-all, Night Willowherb, Scabish, Scurvish, Tree Primrose, Primrose, Moths Moonflower and Primrose Tree. From the family Onagraceae.

A native of North America it was introduced to Europe in 1614 when botanists brought the plant from Virginia as a botanical curiosity. In North America it is regarded as a weed, elsewhere as a pretty garden plant.

The generic name, *Oenothera*, comes from the Greek 'oinos' (wine) and 'thera' (hunt). According to ancient herbals the plant was said to dispel the ill effects of wine, but both plant and seed have been used for other reasons – culinary and medicinal – by American Indians for hundreds of years. The Flambeau Ojibwe tribe were the first to realise its medicinal properties. They used to soak the whole plant in warm water to make a poultice to heal bruises and overcome skin problems. Traditionally, too, it was used to treat asthma, and its medicinal potential is still evolving. Oil of Evening Primrose is currently attracting considerable attention worldwide as a treatment for nervous disorders, in particular Multiple Sclerosis. There may well be a time in the very near future when the pharmaceutical industry will require fields of this beautiful plant to be grown on a commercial scale.

The common name comes from the transformation of its bedraggled daytime appearance into a fragrant, phosphorescent, pale yellow beauty with the opening of its flowers in the early evening. All this show is for one night only, however. Towards the end of summer the flowers tend to stay open all day long. (It is called Evening Star because the petals emit phosphorescent light at night.) Many strains of the plant came to Britain as stowaways in soil used as ballast in cargo ships.

Evening Primrose
Oenothera macrocarpa

SPECIES

Oenothera biennis
Evening Primrose
Hardy biennial. Ht 90-120cm (3-4ft), spread 90cm (3ft). Large evening scented yellow flowers for most of the summer. Long green

Evening Primrose
Oenothera biennis

oval or lance-shaped leaves This is the medicinal herb, and the true herb.

Oenothera macrocarpa (missouriensis)
Hardy perennial. Ht 10cm (4in), spread 40cm (16in) or more. Large yellow bell-shaped flowers, sometimes spotted with red, open at sundown throughout the summer. The small to medium green leaves are of a narrow oblong shape.

Oenothera perennis (Pumila)
Hardy perennial. Ht 15-60cm (6-24in), spread 30cm (12in) Fragrant yellow funnel-shaped flowers all summer. The green leaves are narrow and spoon-shaped.

CULTIVATION

Propagation
Seeds
Sow in early spring on the surface of pots or plug trays, or direct into a prepared site in the garden. Seed is very fine so be careful not to sow it too thick. Use the cardboard method. When the weather has warmed sufficiently, plant out at a distance of 30cm (12in) apart. Often the act of transplanting will encourage the plant to flower the first year. It is a prolific self-seeder. So once introduced into the garden, it will stay.

Pests and Diseases
This plant rarely suffers from pests or disease.

Maintenance
Spring. Sow seed.
Summer. Dead head plants to cut down on self-seeding.
Autumn. Dig up old roots of second-year growth of the biennials.
Winter. No need to protect.

Garden Cultivation
Choose a well-drained soil in a dry, sunny corner for the best results and sow the seeds in late spring to produce flowers the following year. Thin the seedlings to 30cm (12in) apart, when large enough to handle. After the seed is set, the plant dies. It is an extremely tolerant plant, happy in most situations, and I have known seedlings appear in a stone wall, so be forewarned.

Harvest
Use leaves fresh as required. Best before flowering.
Pick the flowers when in bud or when just open. Use fresh. Picked flowers will always close and are no good for flower arrangements.

Collect the seeds as the heads begin to open at the end. Store in jar for sowing in the spring.
Dig up roots and use fresh as a vegetable or to dry.

CONTAINER GROWING

The lower growing varieties are very good in window boxes and tubs. Tall varieties need support from other plants or stakes. None is suitable for growing indoors.

CULINARY

It is a pot herb – roots, stems, leaves, and even flower buds may be eaten. The roots can be boiled – they taste like sweet parsnips, or pickled and tossed in a salad.

MEDICINAL

Soon this plant will take its place in the hall of herbal fame.
It can have startling effects on the treatment of pre-menstrual tension. In 1981 at St Thomas's Hospital, London, 65 women with PMS were treated. 61 per cent experienced complete relief and 23 per cent partial relief. One symptom, breast engorgement, was especially improved – 72 per cent of women reported feeling better. In November 1982,

Evening Primrose *Oenothera biennis*

an edition of the prestigious medical journal *The Lancet* published the results of a double-blind crossover study on 99 patients with ectopic excema, which showed that when high doses of Evening Primrose Oil were taken, about 43 per cent of the patients experienced improvement of their eczema. Studies of the effect of the oil on hyperactive children also indicate that this form of treatment is beneficial.
True to the root of its generic name, the oil does appear to be effective in counteracting alcohol poisoning and preventing hangovers. It can help withdrawal from alcohol, easing depression. It helps dry eyes and brittle nails and, when combined with zinc, the oil may be used to treat acne.
But it is the claim that it benefits sufferers of multiple sclerosis that has brought controversy. It has been recommended for MS sufferers by Professor Field, who directed MS research for the UK Medical Research Council.
Claims go further – that it is effective in guarding against arterial disease; the effective ingredient, gami-linolelic acid (GLA), is a powerful anti-blood clotter, that it aids weight-loss; a New York hospital discovered that people more

than 10 per cent above their ideal body weight lost weight when taking the oil. It is thought that this occurs because the GLA in Evening Primrose Oil stimulates brown fat tissue... and that in perhaps the most remarkable study of all, completed in Glasgow Royal Infirmary in 1987, it helped 60 per cent of patients suffering from rheumatoid arthritis. Those taking fish oil, in addition to Evening Primrose Oil, fared even better.
The scientific explanation for these extraordinary results is that GLA is a precursor of a hormone-like substance called PGE1, which has a wide range of beneficial effects on the body. Production of this substance in some people may be blocked. GLA has also been found in oil extracted from blackcurrant seed and borage seed, both of which are now a commercial source of this substance.

OTHER USES

Leaf and stem can be infused to make an astringent facial steam. Add to hand cream as a softening agent.

Polygonatum multiflorum

SOLOMON'S SEAL

Also known as David's Harp, Jacob's Ladder, Lady's Lockets, Lily of the Mountain, Drop Berry, Seal Root and Sealwort. From the family Lilaceae.

A perennial plant that grows in thick woods and thickets in Europe, Asia and North America.

The plant's generic name, *Polygonatum*, is derived from 'poly', meaning many, and 'gonu', meaning a knee joint, which refers to its many jointed rhizome.

King Solomon, wiser than all men, gave his approval to the use of its roots (said to resemble cut sections of Hebrew characters), as a poultice for wounds, and to help heal broken limbs.

In the 16th century Gerard cited its contribution in the soldering and gluing together broken of bones, when the root might be taken internally (in the form of ale) or applied externally as a poultice.

Solomon's Seal
Polygonatum multiflorum

SPECIES

Polygonatum multiflorum
Solomon's Seal
Hardy perennial. Ht 30-80cm (12-32in), spread 30cm (1ft). White waxy flowers tipped with green hang from arching stems in spring to summer. The berries are bluish-black. The leaves are oval to lance shaped and mid-green in colour.

Polygonatum odoratum
Angular Solomon's Seal
Hardy perennial. Ht 60cm (24in), spread 30cm (12in). Produces pairs of fragrant, tubular, bell-shaped, green-tipped, white flowers in spring. The berries and leaves are as **P. multiflorum**. A variegated form called **Polygonatum odoratum 'Varigatum'**, which has creamy white striped leaves. Also a double-flowered one **Polygonatum odoratum 'Flore Pleno'**, has scented flowers that look rather like ballet dancers' skirts.

Polygonatum verticillatum
Whorled Solomon's Seal
Hardy perennial. Ht 1.2m (48in) spread 45cm (18in). The flowers are narrow and bell shaped, greenish white in colour, and appear in early summer. Its berries are first red, then dark blue.
The lance-shaped, mid-green leaves grow in whorls.

CULTIVATION

Propagation
Seed
Sow fresh seed in autumn into prepared seed or plug trays, cover with the compost, water in well, then cover with glass, and leave outside for the winter. Remove the glass as soon as germination starts in spring. When the seedlings are large enough plant out in a prepared site. Keep an eye on the watering throughout the first season – before they have developed their creeping rhizomes, young plants dry out quickly.

Division
The plant is best divided just after the stalks die down in autumn, although in dampish weather, division and transplanting can be undertaken any time of year. This method is easier and quicker than seeds.

Pests and Diseases
Sawfly caterpillar is a common pest, you will notice that the leaves have clean cut holes. This will not damage the plant but it can

look unsightly if you have a major attack. Spray with a liquid horticultural soap, at the first sign of attack. Complete eradication is difficult.

Maintenance
Spring: Plant out seedlings.
Summer: Make sure the soil does not dry out.
Autumn: Sow fresh seeds. Divide established plants.

Winter: Protect in the event of a prolonged frost below -10°C (14°F).

Garden Cultivation
This elegant graceful plant is sadly becoming scarce. Plant in groups on their own so that the tall and striking arching stems and waxy green-tipped flowers are shown off to their best. It requires a cool shady situation in fertile well-drained soil. Dig the soil over before planting with some leaf mould, and each winter top dress with extra leaf mould.

Harvest
For medicinal use, dig up and dry the roots of a well-established 3-year-old-plant in the autumn after the foliage has died back.

OTHER USES

The plant has been employed cosmetically to clear freckles and as a skin tonic.

In Turkey the young shoots are harvested and cooked with asparagus.

Solomon's Seal *Polygonatum multiflorum* **in flower**

MEDICINAL

The powdered roots and rhizomes make a good poultice for bruises, inflammation and wounds, and a good wash for skin problems and blemishes.

American Indians made a tea of the rootstock to take for women's complaints and general internal pains. They also used it as a wash to counteract the effect of poison ivy.

Polygonatum odoratum contains a substance that lowers the level of blood sugar and has long been used in the Orient for diabetes.

Solomon's seal makes a good skin wash

CONTAINER GROWING

Solomon's Seal can be grown in large containers. Use a soil based compost, and top dress in autumn with well-rotted manure or leaf mould. This will also protect it during winter. Position in semi-shade and water well throughout the summer.

WARNING

All parts of the plant are poisonous and should be taken internally only under supervision of a qualified medicinal or herbal practitioner. Large doses can be harmful.

Sanguisorba minor

SALAD BURNET

Also known as Drumsticks, Old Man's Pepper and Poor Man's Pepper. From the family Rosaceae.

This herb is a native of Europe and Asia. It has been introduced and naturalized in many places elsewhere in the world, especially Britain and the United States. Popular for both its medicinal and culinary properties, it was taken to New England in the Pilgrim Fathers Plant collection and called Pimpernel. It is found in dry, free-draining soil in grassland and on the edges of woodland. The name *Sanguisorba* comes from 'sanguis', meaning blood, and 'sorbere', meaning to soak up. It is an ancient herb which has been grown in this country since the 16th century. Traditionally it was used to staunch wounds. In Tudor times Salad Burnet was planted along borders of garden paths so the scent would rise up when trodden on.

SPECIES

Sanguisorba minor
Salad Burnet
Evergreen hardy perennial. Ht 20-60in (8-24in), spread 30cm (12in). Produces small spikes of dark crimson flowers in summer. Its soft mid-green leaves are divided into oval leaflets.

Sanguisorba officinalis
Great Burnet
Also known as Drumsticks, Maidens Hairs, Red Knobs, and Redheads. Perennial. Ht up to 1.2m (4ft), spread 60cm (2ft). Produces small spikes of dark crimson flowers in summer. Its mid-green leaves are divided into oval leaflets. This wild plant is becoming increasingly rare due to modern farming practices.

CULTIVATION

Propagation
Seed
Sow the small flatish seed in spring or autumn into prepared seed or plug trays and cover the seeds with Perlite; no need for extra heat. If sown in the autumn, winter the seedlings under protection and plant out in spring to a prepared site, 30cm (12in) apart. If spring sown allow to harden off and plant out in the same way. As an edging plant it should be planted at a distance of 20cm (8in) apart.

Division
It divides very easily. Dig up an established plant in the early autumn, cut back any excessive leaves, divide the plant and replant in a prepared site in the garden.

Pests and Diseases
This herb is, in the main, free from pests and diseases.

Maintenance
Spring: Sow seeds.
Summer: Keep cutting to stop it flowering, if being used for culinary purposes.

Salad Burnet
Sanguisorba minor

Autumn: Sow seeds if necessary. Divide established plants.
Winter: No protection needed, fully hardy.

Garden Cultivation

This is a most attractive, soft-leaf evergreen and is very useful in both kitchen and garden. That it is evergreen is a particular plus for the herb garden, where it looks most effective as an edging plant. It also looks good in a wild flower garden, where it grows as happily as in its original grassland habitat.

The art with this plant is to keep cutting, which stops it flowering and encourages lots of new growth.

With no special requirements, it prefers chalky soil, but it will tolerate any well-drained soil in sun or light shade. It is deep rooting and very drought resistant.

Harvest

Pick young tender leaves when required. Not necessary to dry leaves (which in any case do not dry well), as fresh leaves can be harvested all year round.

CONTAINER GROWING

Salad Burnet will grow in containers, and will provide an excellent source of soft evergreen leaves throughout winter for those with no garden. Use a soil-based compost. Water regularly, but not too frequently; feed with liquid fertilizer in the spring only. Do not over-feed otherwise the leaf will soften and lose its cool cucumber flavour, becoming more like a spinach. For regular use the plant should not be allowed to flower. Cut back constantly to about 15cm (6in) to ensure a continuing supply of tender new leaves.

CULINARY

Leaves have a nutty flavour and a slight taste of cucumber. The young leaves are refreshing in salads and can be used generously – they certainly enhance winter salads. Tender young leaves can also be added to soups, cold drinks, cream cheeses, or used (like parsley) as a garnish or to flavour casseroles – add at the beginning of cooking. The leaves also make an interesting herbal vinegar.

Salad Burnet combines with other herbs, especially rosemary and tarragon. Serve in a sauce with white fish.

Salad Burnet *Sanguisorba minor*

OTHER USES

Because of its high tannin content, the root of Great Burnet can be used in the tanning of leather.

WARNING

Great Burnet should never be taken in large doses.

This recipe is for a herb butter, which is lovely with grilled fish, either cooked under the grill or on the barbecue, and gives a cucumber flavour to the butter.

75g (3oz) butter
1½ tablespoons chopped Salad Burnet
1 tablespoon chopped garden mint (spearmint)
Salt and black pepper
Lemon juice

Mix the chopped herb leaves together. Melt the butter in a saucepan, add the herbs and simmer on a very low heat for 10 minutes. Season the sauce to taste with salt and pepper, and a squeeze (no more) of lemon. Pour over grilled fish (plaice or sole).

Salad Burnet butter

MEDICINAL

Chewing the leaf assists digestion. An infusion of the whole plant is used for treating haemorrhoids and diarrhoea.

Tanacetum parthenium (Chrysanthemum parthenium)

FEVERFEW

Known in America as Featherfew and Febrifuge Plant. From the family Compositae.

Feverfew was probably a native of south-east Europe and spread via the Mediterranean to many parts of the world, including Britain and North America. It is an attractive and robust, vigorous plant, and is found growing in the wild on dry, well-drained soils.

Its common name suggests that the herb was used in the treatment of fevers. It is said to be derived from the Latin 'febrifugia', meaning a substance that drives out fevers. The old herbalists even call it a febrifuge. However, strange as it may seem, the herb was hardly ever employed for the purpose.

Gerard, the Elizabethan herbalist, advised use of the dried plant for 'those that are giddied in the head or have vertigo'. In the 17th century Culpeper advised its use for pains in the head and colds. In the late 18th century it was considered a special remedy for a body racked by too much opium. Nowadays it is used in the treatment of migraines.

SPECIES

Tanacetum parthenium (Chrysanthemum parthenium)
Feverfew
Hardy perennial. Ht 60cm-1.2m (2-4ft), spread 45cm (18in). White daisy-like flowers from early summer to early autumn. The leaf is mid-green, and a typical chrysanthemum shape.

Tanacetum parthenium 'White Bonnet'
Double-Flowered Feverfew
Hardy perennial. Ht 30cm (12in), spread 45cm (18in). Double white flowers, otherwise as **T. parthenium**.

Tanacetum parthenium 'Aureum'
Golden Feverfew
Hardy perennial. Ht and spread 20-45cm (8-18in). Gold green leaves that remain colourful all year. Otherwise as **T. parthenium**. Growth and colour make Golden Feverfew popular as an edging plant in formal herb gardens and as a partier filling. Particularly conspicuous in winter.

Feverfew *Tanacetum parthenium*

CULTIVATION

Propagation
Seeds
Fine, thin and fairly small, they tend to stick together especially if they get damp. Mix a very small amount of seed with an equally small amount of Perlite or dry sand to make sowing easier. Sow very thinly in spring or early autumn, directly into pots or plug trays. Cover with a final thin layer of Perlite. Germination is usually very rapid, 7-10 days. No need for extra heat. Plant out 30cm (12in) apart, as soon as the seedlings are large enough to handle and hardened off. If sown in autumn, the young plants will need to be wintered under protection.

Division
Dig up established clumps in early autumn. Ease the plants apart, and either replant directly in the positions required or pot up in a standard pot or fancy container for flowers in late spring. Winter in a cold greenhouse or cold frame. Use the bark, peat compost.

Cuttings
Take stem cuttings in the summer, making sure there are no flowers on the cutting material.

Pests and Diseases
Unaffected by the majority of pests and diseases, golden feverfew can suffer from sun scorch; if this occurs cut back and the new growth will be unaffected.

Maintenance
Spring: Sow seeds.
Summer: As flowering finishes cut plant back to restore shape, and remove all flowering heads to minimize self-seeding.
Autumn: Divide established clumps. This is the best time for sowing if edging plants are required. Winter young plants in a cold frame.
Winter: No need to protect, fully frost hardy.

Garden Cultivation
Feverfew, while tolerant by nature, is an invasive plant, so choose the site with care. It will grow anywhere, in nooks or crannies, but likes best a loam soil enriched with good manure in a sunny position. Seeds can be sown direct into a prepared site in late spring. When the seedlings are large enough to handle thin to 30cm (12in) apart.

Harvest
Pick leaves before the plant flowers; dry if required for use medicinally. Pick the flowers just as they open; dry hanging upside down.

CONTAINER GROWING

Grown indoors, the plants get stretched and leggy. However, in containers outside all the feverfews flourish. Golden Feverfew, having the most compact habit, looks very effective in a hanging basket, tub or window-box. Use the bark, peat mix of compost. Keep the plants regularly watered and feed during flowering. Cut back plants after flowering as this will help maintain their shape.

CULINARY

The young leaves of feverfew can be added to salads, but be warned they are very bitter so add sparingly.

MEDICINAL

That feverfew has a propensity to overcome melancholy has been known by herbalists for centuries. However, its ability to soothe headaches was not given much attention until the 1970s when it was thoroughly investigated scientifically, following claims that it reduced migraines. Many clinical trials were held and results, over a six-month period, showed a 70 per cent reduction in migraines, and 43 per cent of the patients felt other beneficial side-effects, including more restful sleep and relief from arthritis. 18 per cent had unpleasant side effects. Golden and double-flowered forms have not been tested, though experience suggests that they will react similarly.

Eat 3 to 5 fresh leaves between a slice of bread every day to reduce migraines. As mentioned before, this is very bitter, so put the leaves in a sandwich (brown bread, of course). To make it more palatable, you could add a sprig of mint, marjoram or parsley. Do NOT eat more.

OTHER USES

A decoction or infusion of the leaves is a mild disinfectant, and the leaves in sachets make a good moth repellent.

WARNING

One side effect associated with taking feverfew is ulceration of the mouth.

Feverfew in sachets makes a good moth repellant

Valeriana officinalis

VALERIAN

Also known as All Heal, Set All, Common Valerian, Garden Heliotrope, Cut Finger, Fragrant Valerian, Cat's Valerian and St. George's Herb. From the family Valerianaceae.

Valerian is a native of Europe and West Asia and is now naturalized in North America. It is found in grasslands, ditches, damp meadows and close to streams.

The name may come from the Latin 'valere' to be healthy, an allusion to its powerful medicinal qualities. Or from an early herbalist, Valeris, who first used it medicinally.

Fresh valerian roots smell like ancient leather, but when dried they smell more like stale sweat. In spite of this, valerian is still used to add a musky tone to perfume. Cats and rats are attracted to the smell and The Pied Piper of Hamelin is said to have carried the root. A tincture of valerian was employed in the First and Second World Wars to treat shell-shock and nervous stress.

COMPANION PLANTING

If planted near other vegetables, it boosts their growth by stimulating phosphorus and earthworm activity.

OTHER USES

Infuse root and spray on the ground to attract earthworms. Add mineral-rich leaves to new compost. Use the root in rat traps.

MEDICINAL

The root is a calmative. Its sedative and anti-spasmodic effects are of benefit in the treatment of a wide range of nervous disorders and intestinal colic.

Decoct the root or, more effectively, crush 1 teaspoon (5ml) of dried root and soak in cold water for 12-24 hours. Drink as a sedative for mild insomnia, sudden emotional distress, headaches, intestinal cramps and nervous exhaustion.

SPECIES

Valeriana officinalis
Valerian
Hardy perennial. Ht 1-1.2m (3-4ft), spread 1m (3ft). Pale pink/white flowerheads in summer. Leaves deeply toothed and mid-green.

CULTIVATION

Propagation
Seed
Sow the fairly small seeds in early spring, either in seed or plug trays. Press the seeds into the soil but do not cover, as this will delay germination. When the seedlings are large enough to handle, transplant to the garden at a distance of 60cm (24in) apart.

Valerian *Valeriana officinalis*

Division
Divide the roots in spring or autumn. Replant after division in a prepared site.

Pests and Diseases
Valerian is mostly free from pests and disease.

Maintenance
Spring: Sow seed. Divide roots.
Summer: Cut back after flowering to prevent self-seeding.
Autumn: Divide establish plants if needed.
Winter: A very hardy plant, no need for protection.

Garden Cultivation
Valerian is one of the earliest flowering, tall, wetland plants. As long as its roots are kept cool. (which is why it prefers to be near water) it can be grown successfully in almost any garden soil in sun or deep shade, You can sow seeds direct in spring, leaving uncovered, but for a more guaranteed result start off in plug trays. Remember that cats love the scent when choosing the planting site

Harvest
Dig up complete root in late autumn of the second and third years. Wash and remove the pale fibrous roots, leaving the edible rhizome. To dry this rhizome, cut it into manageable slices (see drying).

WARNING

Valerian should not be taken in large doses for an extended period of time.